# TEACHING Tricky Bits

## SCIENCE

# Plants and Animals

John Stringer

Published by
Hopscotch Educational Publishing Ltd,
29 Waterloo Place,
Leamington Spa CV32 5LA
Tel: 01926 744227

© 2001 Hopscotch Educational Publishing

Written by John Stringer
Series design by Blade Communications
Illustrated by Bernard Connors
Printed by Clintplan, Southam

ISBN 1-902239-71-7

# Contents

# About the series

**Teaching the Tricky Bits** arose out of a frustrated teacher's cry for help when one of the children in her class said 'But why do we need blood?' She sort-of knew the answer but couldn't quite explain it so that the child could understand.

So the concept of a series of books that would inform teachers about the different science topics in the National Curriculum began to be developed.

But soon we realised that often information on science tends to be dry and can only be taken in in bite-sized pieces for fear of falling asleep. So we needed a series of books that would keep teachers informed and awake!

This is what we have achieved. This book and the other three in the series all contain vital, useful and fascinating information written by John Stringer, a member of the primary committee of the Association for Science Education and well-known author of science materials. But just as important as the information John has supplied

is the approach he has taken with his writing – it's fun to read! There are amusing scenarios and anecdotes. You really won't fall asleep!

Then we realised that it's all well and good having all this information and rolling about in the aisles laughing, but what are you going to do with it? Or, more importantly, what are the children going to do with your new-found knowledge?

So, John has provided relevant activities for each chapter, starting with what could be done at level 1 and going all the way to level 5.

This makes these books ideal for every teacher. You can allocate activities according to ability. You can still use the book if you find yourself teaching a different age group.

We hope you enjoy reading and using this book as much as we have enjoyed putting it together!

Other titles in the series are:

### Forces, electricity and magnetism
(and the Earth in space)

ISBN 1 902239 69 5

### Materials

ISBN 1 902239 70 9

### The Human Body

ISBN 1 902239 68 7

# Introduction

## Do animals need plants?

We certainly do! Without plants, animals, including us humans, wouldn't survive – and I don't mean just because we eat them!

If we were dependent on the stored oxygen in the atmosphere for breathing, life on Earth would be finite. When the last of the oxygen had been used up (or actually, long before) life on Earth (except for minute creatures that can live without it) would end. Even if we were to stop being so wasteful with the stuff – burning it, or pumping it through our forms of transport – it would not last for ever. It has to be renewed. Fortunately for us, the green plants – including the algae that live in the seas and in fresh water – are very good at that. All our oxygen is recycled – again and again.

I said that we would die long before the oxygen ran out. The reason for that is that the waste gas we breathe out – carbon dioxide – is poisonous in large quantities, and a build-up in the atmosphere would kill us. Fortunately, plants have a use for carbon dioxide. They recycle that too, using it to make food for themselves (and often, for animals) and producing (guess what) oxygen!

This handy cycle ensures that life on Earth can continue indefinitely. True, plants need oxygen too, and yes, they produce some carbon dioxide, but this is far outweighed by the amount of oxygen they produce.

### Fascinating facts

- The Red Queen hypothesis says that an advance by any species damages the environment for all the others. They end up disadvantaged unless they, too, make advances to keep up. 'It takes all the running you can do to keep in the same place,' as the Red Queen says in 'Alice'. We are the species to have made the greatest single advance, of course.

So, the relationship between plants and animals is in balance. Some scientists have suggested that the Earth itself somehow strives to keep this balance – an idea called the 'Gaia theory'. One thing is certain – green plants are essential to the cycle.

### And – they give us more than just oxygen!

We don't need plants just for gases. We can eat them (or we eat the animals that eat plants) and we use plant products for clothes, shelter, furniture and medicines.

So, without plants there would be no animal life on Earth. We need them. It is this complex relationship between plants and animals that makes their study so interesting.

It is the breakdown of this relationship, by pollution and the wholesale destruction of the rainforests, that threatens us and all other living things.

# Do plants need animals?

You wouldn't think so, would you? Everything they need is right there where they are growing. They have carbon dioxide from the air, water from the rain and a pinch of mineral salts from the soil. Combining all these produces a living growing thing.

So, do animals do anything for plants? Well yes, they do. First of all, they produce a large part of the carbon dioxide needed for plants to photosynthesise and live.

And, just as important, animals provide a useful delivery system for living things that are literally rooted to the spot. If you have some dusty yellow pollen that you are keen to get to that plant over there, then what better way than hitching a lift on a furry insect travelling from flower to flower? Usefully, the honey-bee has very casual standards of personal hygiene – and no clothes to brush. So it will fly off with pollen on its coat. Indeed, plants can even afford to sacrifice a bit as bee food – hence the pollen sacs on the bee's legs. Plants provide a few encouragements – sweet nectar, bright colours and even markings (bee lines) that help with a safe landing.

Bees, flies and other insects, some birds and other animals offer this helpful service – and it doesn't stop there. When the pollen has been delivered, the egg has been fertilised and the seeds have formed, they need distributing, too. So animals provide a convenient – if erratic – delivery service for seeds.

## Fascinating facts

- 70 per cent of the Earth's surface is water. Algae floating near the surface of the sea make a huge contribution to the oxygen in the atmosphere.

- Plants may not move, but they can communicate. Trees attacked by parasites release a chemical that warns their neighbours in the wood about the invasion.

The outsides of animals – the fur of mammals and the feathers of birds – provide a convenient hanging place for hooked burrs and sticky seeds. The insides will accept tasty fruits and, if the seeds are resistant to digestion (with a hard coat), then they will pass through the eater and be deposited somewhere far away, together with some waste matter rich in organic material (otherwise known as manure).

Many seeds are transported like this. Even the huge stones of the avocado tree are carried away by the birds that eat the fruit – though it is probably just as well that they don't pass right through the bird but are regurgitated. Otherwise the resplendent quetzal bird might be famed for its constipation!

It's as if the fruits of many seeds had a sign hanging on them saying 'Eat me.' Their colour, taste and smell are all inviting and it doesn't take long before an animal accepts their invitation. And if they don't? Well, the fruit falls to the ground with its precious packet of seeds and may germinate anyway. But, without the animals – especially the birds – that feast on their fruits and carelessly drop their seeds from the skies, a lot of plants would be rooted to the spot in every sense.

# Living together

So things are arranged so that each side benefits from the other. It's easy to forget, especially if you live in an urban environment, that this natural world underpins our very lives. When your food comes prepacked, and the only plants you see are in parks and flower shops, you can overlook the close relationship we all have with the natural world. Perhaps that's why we choose to take breaks in the countryside and succumb to the attraction of gardening. These activities bring us closer to the plants and animals we depend on.

# Imagine a world without plants

We know it's not possible because they provide the oxygen we need, but just imagine for a moment that all plant products were eliminated from your busy urban life. You can forget your breakfast – cereal, bread and jam will disappear. But it's not just vegetarians who will suffer; the cow that provided your milk and butter needed plant food and the animals that added the protein to your meal will have eaten plants.

And, sorry, but you'll have no furniture to sit on. Wood is a plant product, of course, and even plastic materials are made from a material (oil) that originated from plant life.

Finally, it is just as well if you are not too modest. Most of your clothes (cotton, linen) are plant products – and the woollen ones come from sheep that feed on grass.

So, no matter how much we may think we are divorced from nature, we are a part of it. It's vital that we, and our children, appreciate this unending dependence. It's the first step towards environmental responsibility.

# Now imagine a world without animals

I'll not even mention the food they provide for many people.

What about the milk from the cows? No cheese – heavens above! No honey! No eggs (no cakes, no soufflés, no Yorkshire puddings – I could go on!).

What, no wool for our jumpers? (And, yes, we get leather from animals, too.)

Imagine – no horses to ride, no dogs to walk, no cats to stroke, no birds to sing, no wildlife programmes on the telly!

And animals also help us with medicines, transport, law and order…

# Is there life on Earth?

There certainly is! Earth is packed with living things. Every plant and animal lives in an environment and the Earth is a huge environment. Another name for this environment is the 'biosphere'.

## The biosphere

The **biosphere** is the part of our Earth that supports life – the land, the water and the lower part of the atmosphere.

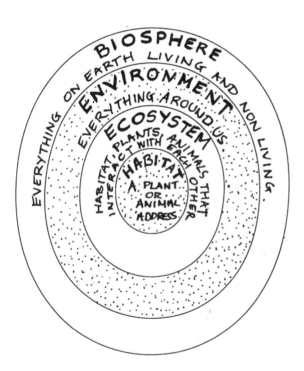

## An environment

We use the word 'environment' to describe our surroundings on Earth. Our **environment** is everything that affects us – the place where we live, our home and school, our mild but sometimes rainy weather, our food, water and the air we breathe, the plants and animals we affect and that affect us, the special animals we call our friends and family – and also the strangers whose work and behaviour affect us.

## A habitat

The part of the environment surrounding each plant or animal, which provides all that it needs, is called the **habitat** of the plant or animal – the place where it lives. A plant's habitat is its address – the place where it lives. An animal's habitat is its address, too. But because most animals move around, an animal's habitat will be wider and bigger. A cave, a woodland, a pond or a forest floor are all habitats. So are canals, gardens, playgrounds and even walls.

Habitats are places that provide: a source of raw materials for growth and activity; a source of energy, either from the Sun or from the plants that harness the Sun's energy; shelter from changing conditions, from weather and from predators; and a place to dump the products of living.

## The ecosystem

The plants and animals in a habitat are linked through food chains and webs. The animals may live by eating plants found in their habitat, or by eating other animals that in turn eat the plants. This link between plants and animals and their habitat is called an **ecosystem**.

Lions eat gazelles that eat the green plants found on the African plains. They are in the same ecosystem. Gazelles don't eat seaweed and lions don't eat penguins. They are not found in their habitat and so are not a part of their ecosystem.

Ecosystems are about energy flow. Forget any romantic view of nature. Think of the plants and animals as links in this flow of energy. The first link in this chain is the green plant kingdom. Plants capture the Sun's energy through a process called photosynthesis (see page 19), whereby they make their own food. This energy is passed on to animals who eat the plants (herbivores) and then to meat-eating animals that eat the herbivores (carnivores). At any stage, nutrients are returned to the soil through the decomposition of waste – excrement and dead bodies – and the cycle is complete. So even the soil and the physical surroundings are part of the pattern.

### Save the rainforest – wear a hat!

This is not an efficient process – because each link in the chain needs to keep some for itself. The plants need to live and grow. So do the animals. In addition, creatures like us need to stay warm – an expensive business in

### Fascinating facts

- Sometimes adaptations lead to completely new plants or animals. The finches on the Galapagos Islands probably came from one original group but as they travelled to different islands, each finch changed to suit its new home. Now there are 13 different Galapagos finches, each one suited to its special habitat.

terms of energy. We can waste a lot of this energy as heat loss, too. All these are interrelated. You could argue that wearing a hat (to retain heat in your head) is one way of saving the rainforest.

The whole thing is pretty fragile. The removal of just one species can unravel the ecosystem with terrifying speed. That's why environmental protesters can get so hot under the collar. Take, for example, the spread of myxomatosis among rabbits. This disease was welcomed by farmers when it began to wipe out these cuddly pests. But the decimation of the rabbit population was catastrophic for foxes, who began to look for food elsewhere, wandering suburban streets in search of full dustbins. At the other end of the scale, wild plant populations exploded, uncropped by rabbits. Suppose the fox population had been wiped out instead. The result would have been an explosion of rabbit numbers (remember they would breed like rabbits!) and the green plants would be grazed to extinction. And then the starving rabbits would begin to die …

### Just another bypass

Of course the biggest ecosystem destroyer has two legs – and giant earthmovers and an unlimited supply of concrete. When a new road is pushed through a habitat, it rattles not just the plants and animals living there, but others that depend upon them. Well-meaning conservationists have attempted to save habitats by moving them – rolling up a meadow to make room for a supermarket, for example. But other factors – the soil, the exposure, the microclimate – are different, and these projects are seldom successful. It's not just the plants and animals that matter. It's every aspect of the ecosystem. The more we learn about the environment, the more we discover how closely everything is interlinked.

## Biodiversity

Only humans can adapt to almost any habitat. By wearing special clothes, living in special shelters or using technology, humans can live at the North Pole or in a desert, can go underwater or can fly.

Each plant and each animal suits the place where it lives. You don't find monkeys under the sea, or fish up trees. Monkeys and fish are adapted to their habitats.

An adaptation is a change in the way that plants or animals are shaped that suits them to their habitat. For example, while the eagle cannot reach the nectar inside flowers, it can soar high in the skies and has wonderful eyesight to help it spot its prey and fierce talons and a beak to catch it. The humming-bird cannot catch and eat other birds but it is so tiny and has such an amazing speed of wing flapping that it can hover over flowers to feed on the nectar (and they can fly backwards – the only bird that can!).

Many animals fly but they fly in different ways. Hawk-moths can fly at 45km an hour to escape predators. Swifts have small wings, adapted to flying at 170km an hour to catch flying insects. Albatross don't fly so fast. Their huge wings – up to four metres across – are adapted to enable them to soar and glide for long periods.

All these different flying animals are adapted to living in different habitats. Each exploits its own environmental niche – usually very successfully, until some human comes along and messes it up.

### The amazing dandelion

Some living things are amazingly adaptable. The dandelion – sometimes called 'the children's flower' – is a real toughie, partly because of its long taproot. This goes down so far that it can find water even in very dry conditions. That's why the dandelions on your lawn stay green even if the grass is dry and brown. And, of course, if you leave the smallest bit of root in the ground, the plant will regenerate from that. Add to these survival

techniques the ability to parachute its seeds into enemy territory several kilometres from home, and you will see why the dandelion is the Rambo of the plant world. It can even change its structure to suit its surroundings.

The dandelion is far from dull; its flower head is made up of hundreds of individual flowers; dandelions are cultivated in France as a salad vegetable, and there is some truth in rumours of its diuretic qualities. But it's the plant's adaptability that is remarkable. Not many plants can match it for its toughness.

### Invasion of the plants

Some living things can adapt to living in many different habitats. They can cross habitat lines, turning up in surprising places. Plants and insects can be fairly undemanding, growing and living in the most unlikely places – cracks in walls or chimney pots. Changes we make to the habitat can offer them great opportunities. The rosebay willow-herb and the senecio plants are classic cases.

The old steam trains started frequent trackside fires, clearing great areas of land. Plants and animals quickly invaded the open land, and there was fierce competition for these rich and undisturbed areas. Plants like the rosebay willow-herb became known as 'fireweed' because they so quickly colonised and exploited the burned environment, with their floating wind-borne seeds that hang around them like beards.

*rosebay willow-herbs*

Senecio, a plant that had been introduced to the Bodleian Museum in Oxford from Mount Etna, crossed the museum wall and found, in the cinders of the railway track outside, conditions exactly like home. It spread rapidly along the convenient 'roads' presented to it by the railway network, and is now established all over the country.

Insects can benefit from this change. The cinnabar moth, with its bright yellow and black striped caterpillar, feeds on senecio, and can be found in millions on newly-cleared ground. Cinnabar caterpillar droppings help fertilise the next generation of senecio. After the Second World War, cinnabar populations exploded as the caterpillar found good feeding grounds among the rubble of bombed houses.

## Changing habitats

Habitats change naturally. They may change daily, when the Sun comes up and goes down, or the tide goes in and out. They may change with the seasons, as it turns first cold and then warm again. They may change completely over short periods of time – after an earthquake, a flood or a volcanic eruption. They may change completely over a longer period of time, as a river changes course or rocks wear away. Ponds dry up, trees die and are replaced by new young trees, and grass withers in a hot summer.

Habitats are also changed by outside influences. Faced with yet another grazed knee, the headteacher of a primary school decided that the uneven paving slabs would have to go. A smooth layer of asphalt was the answer – no breaks, no gaps, no edges to trip over. The job was quickly done; but a small habitat was destroyed. The small plants that had a grip on the thin soil between the slabs; the ants that had nested in the soft bedding sand; the worms, beetles and other small invertebrates that lived under and between the stones.

### Fascinating facts

- A bird called the shearwater makes a journey of nearly 32,000km every year when it migrates.

- A billion people in over a hundred countries are threatened by the spread of deserts.

- The overuse of land in Iceland has led to a 5,000 square kilometre barren zone and a further 37,000 square kilometres are under threat.

The birds that were occasional visitors – the thrush that had found both snails and a handy anvil and the woodpecker that had feasted on ants when the tree insects were few, had gone. So the caretaker's cat no longer lurked with a view to catching a bird.

We can't help environmental change – but we can be sensitive to the rolling effects of our actions. On a much larger scale, 'desertification' is the process that renders fertile land arid and dead. Around the world, a hundred square kilometres are lost to desert every day. In Africa, a series of droughts has enlarged the Sahara southwards. These droughts may be linked to world climate change. But heavy grazing and deeper wells have disturbed the fertile Sahel region, so that the Sahara is growing at around 5km a year.

So, habitats are always changing. Most plants and animals can adapt to small changes in their habitat. But some cannot. Most animals can move when the habitat changes, and find somewhere else to live. Plants cannot. Animals may survive seasonal change by migrating, or by hibernating. Big changes to a habitat can destroy populations of animals and plants. Some of those big changes are made by people.

You can't make changes in your garden without an environmental impact. Try looking at Charlie Dimmock and Alan Titchmarsh as habitat changers, and you will see what I mean.

## Migration

There are three ways of handling habitat change – you can grin and bear it (adapting to it if you can), you can sleep through it, or you can get up and go. This seasonal or periodic mass movement of animals is called migration, and it is the reaction of animals that cannot change their bodies – growing more fur or feathers, changing their colour – or change their habits when the place they live in becomes unfriendly.

Birds from Great Britain fly south for the winter; herds of animals travel great distances to warmer parts of North America.

While we usually think of birds migrating, insects, fish and mammals migrate too – monarch butterflies migrate, fish return to their birth rivers, seals journey to islands where they breed and wildebeest annually migrate from Kenya to northern South Africa (on the way, they provide a food source for Nile crocodiles).

Migrating birds cover huge distances – the Arctic tern breeds close to the North Pole and winters in the Antarctic.

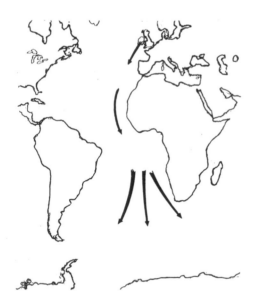

*The migration route of the Arctic tern*

Children will be aware of the annual gatherings of migratory birds on trees and power lines, ready for flight. There is no definitive explanation of the mechanism of migration. Changes in conditions trigger the migratory urge. Birds appear to navigate by the Sun and stars; they may also be sensitive to the magnetic field of the Earth and the effects of its rotation about its axis. Traces of iron have been found in the brain tissue of birds, seeming to confirm the magnetic theory. This magnetic compass has

### Fascinating facts

- The migration of some salmon includes an upriver journey of 4,000km.

- American monarch butterflies may make round-trips of 8,000km to avoid the cold north, travelling south during the day and then resting in their winter sites for up to five months.

- Scientists suspected that adult starlings guided the migration of their young. They removed the adults from a flock of starlings, and the young birds got lost.

- Most bird migration takes place over 3,000 metres up in the sky – where we can't see it.

- A migrating herd of springbok in 19th century Africa contained over a million animals.

been found in homing honey-bees and even in some bacteria that use it to decide which way is 'down'. They may also use memories of features on the route, though this would not explain the unerring migration of young birds – unless some hereditary instinct is involved. Recently, desert-living ants, which may spend the morning wandering apparently aimlessly – and in every direction – have been observed heading unerringly for home – in a straight line – the moment it looked like rain. This useful skill is one we can't duplicate in the supermarket or a large car park!

### Salmon climb ladders

The migration of salmon is a stunning example of these incredible journeys. Salmon eggs may hatch in a river in Scotland. These young salmon somehow know that this is not the place to spawn – and they make a transatlantic journey to spawn in the Sargasso Sea, thousands of miles from their birthplace, with other salmon drawn there from all over the world. Having spawned, the female salmon, ripe with eggs, makes the journey back to

Scotland. There she makes her way up her birth river – braving fast-flowing flood waters, 'salmon ladders' constructed to bypass hydroelectric dams, animal predators and fishermen – and finally lays her eggs where she herself was hatched. How does she do this? She must be sensitive to currents and tiny changes in water composition and temperature. She must be able to recognise the water where she was born in the same way that we can recognise our home and our family.

## Hibernation

Some animals, like bears, sleep through the difficult times. They hibernate. They may adapt, too – some grow a coat of white fur in snowy weather. Most do not sleep the whole time – they wake to eat. Hibernating mammals are inactive, with a lowered body temperature; but other physiological changes vary with the species.

Even cold-blooded animals may hibernate – amphibians and reptiles become torpid; some insects have glycerol (antifreeze) in their blood, allowing them to tolerate below-freezing temperatures. Birds cannot hibernate – they lack the insulation to survive long, cold winters – but they may have daily periods of reduced metabolism when everything slows down (you may know how they feel!).

### Absent-minded squirrels

It is a fallacy that animals hibernate all the winter. A winter walk will show you – even in big city parks – that squirrels are active all through the cold weather. (And incidentally, they are no Einsteins when it comes to acorn stores. They don't seem to go back to the place they tucked away their supplies – they are just as likely to dig up somebody else's. It looks as if they just identify good storage spots and dig there – and if they find another squirrel's collection, chances are that squirrel is eating theirs.)

A dormouse has a brain thermostat, like all the other warm-blooded mammals – but as winter approaches, it curls up so that there is less surface to its body from which to lose heat. It turns down its body thermostat to around 4°C – about the temperature of your fridge. Its heartbeat slows from 300 beats a minute to 10 beats a minute, and it trickles the energy in its stored fat into its systems to keep them on tick-over. This trick has earned it a name not unrelated to the word 'dormitory' and a reputation that put it in the teapot in 'Alice'.

If the temperature doesn't drop, then animals don't hibernate. Bears in warm zoos, fed by keepers, entertain visitors throughout the winter. They don't need to hibernate.

It's not just big, furry animals that hibernate. Seeds do it, bees do it, even insects in the trees do it. Ladybirds, for example, huddle together in a sleep-like state we call torpor. Butterflies find undusted corners of our window frames and sink into this sleep. The pupa or cocoon stage is a handy way of passing the winter for many insects. Living off the food that they accumulated as larvae, they emerge as adults when the weather gets warmer in the spring.

### Can't abide the heat

Many plants and animals 'hibernate' when the conditions become too warm, or too dry – a long sleep called 'aestivation'. Desert animals like tortoises and frogs can fill their bodies with water (so that half their body weight is a water store) and pull the duvet over their heads. The African lung-fish – a fish that can't decide whether it wants to live in water or on land and has found a handy niche between the two – can curl up in a tunnel in dried mud, breathing through a hole, and wait up to four years for things to get better. Lung-fish could miss an entire term of government and still wake up to vote. In fact a handy way of sending lung-fish to zoos is to can them – mud and all – and send them through the post. Not the kind of tin to open when you need a quick meal!

## Extinction

But animals that cannot adapt to changed conditions die out. And because humans have been responsible for more environmental change than any other factor, humans have been responsible for a great many extinctions. More animals have become extinct in the past 300 years than in all the years before because of humans. We have changed habitats by farming, clearing trees and building roads and houses. Animals like the dodo, the Tasmanian wolf and the Balinese tiger have died out.

Some of the most major changes are the result of 'The Human Factor'. By our use of land, we can change habitats and affect the lives of plants and animals. Our changes may be damaging – green field site development – or for the better – the landscaping of old industrial sites. We are learning to protect environments, recognising the delicacy of environmental balance and the vulnerability of the natural world.

This may go against your lifestyle. You may be an inner-city dweller who never sees a blade of grass. But you are as dependent on the environment as anybody. And remember – nowhere is without life. You just need to get out more and look around you!

### We can't stop change

We are rightly concerned about environmental change – and especially environmental damage. But we would be wrong to think that habitats are unchanging. Every habitat is changing – even without human intervention – and animals and plants unable to survive these changes – annual, seasonal, or daily – would soon be extinct.

Animals and plants have evolved structures and lifestyles that enable them to survive, feed and reproduce. But they also have to cope with changes in the habitat. The animals on a seashore have to survive the movement of the tide, twice every day, that will plunge them underwater and then leave them exposed to the Sun. Many plants and animals respond to daily change. Animals may be nocturnal – like classroom hamsters – and plants like the daisy close in the evening. They may be affected by seasonal change – hibernating in the winter, or migrating in the summer. Natural disasters, and slow natural changes, affect plants and animals.

## Fascinating facts

- Brine shrimps – the little items you can buy in toy shops as 'sea monkeys' – can survive 100 years in their tough coats and still emerge active and lively the moment there is a drop of rain or we tip them from their packet into an aquarium.

- Bears don't really hibernate like dormice. They are in a kind of deep sleep. Their temperature seldom drops below 15°C, and they are quite active – even giving birth to their young in the hibernation period.

- Snow can keep you warm. Many birds and small mammals use snow as an insulator. Lemmings tunnel under snow, feeding on roots and seeds. The air between the snow crystals acts as a thermal insulator – and of course the lemmings are out of the wind!

# Activities

## Level One

Go on a scavenger hunt. Look at the variety of plants and animals around you. You need a safe, clean, enclosed or controllable natural area. You may need to make a list of things to find in your school grounds. Seize the opportunity to teach the children about environmental care; only to collect a tiny part of very common plants, for example.

## Level Two

Explore habitat change. Ask the children to lay a couple of metres of string across the ground, and then to follow it in 'Honey I shrunk the Kids' style from end to end. They will find hand lenses useful and you can provide paper for them to record – perhaps on a long line – what they find near the string. They may observe the way that plant types change as you get deeper under the shadow of a tree, or the way the soil itself changes across a path through the grass. Record the results as drawings – and name what you can. It's the differences that matter. This is great fun, and can be a stimulus to stories and discussion, too. Expect, and accept, a wide variety of responses and ways of responding – pictures, poetry, drama. Perhaps scientific recording should embrace other styles.

## Level Three

Make a small habitat change. Putting a small carpet square – a shop sample is ideal – on an area of rough ground or grassland will make a small but significant environmental change. Discuss with the children what might happen. Then try putting a small square of carpet on the school field. Leave it for a week. Then lift it slowly. Look underneath.

Ask the children 'What has happened to the plants? Are they still green? How have they grown?'

'What animals have come to the carpet square? What animals choose the dark and damp? What do they do when you lift the carpet square?'

This leads to an investigation. Try some small mobile animals – woodlice are ideal – and ask the children to find out whether they prefer light or dark. Give them a box and a torch if they need a clue. If they use a set

number of animals – say ten – and repeat their activity several times, they could produce statistical results.

## Level Four

Explore how habitat differences can change the plants that live there. Dandelions can differ so much in appearance from the centre of a field (where they can form a flat, dry rosette) to the edges (where they can be tall and verdant) that they can look like two different plants. Transplanted plants respond to the new conditions – more water and less sunlight at the field edge. Dandelions stay green in the driest conditions, of course, because of that long taproot.

## Level Five

We protect habitats that we want to keep unchanged. One way of doing this is to create a nature reserve. Use this activity to create the smallest nature reserve on Earth! But notice that even creating a nature reserve means making changes! Give each pair of children a metre of string, tied in a loop. They put their loop on the ground and it becomes the border of their miniature nature reserve. They can put natural objects inside it – stones, twigs, scraps of dead leaf – but they mustn't harm living things as they 'furnish' their reserve. They can create a front gate, car park, cafe and loos, a resting place, an adventure playground, an animal enclosure. Children of all ages get great delight from this and it is especially helpful if you are trying to teach them how maps can represent an area – they can get a bird's-eye view of their reserve, and draw a scale plan of it.

At this level, children should be able to explain that different organisms are found in different habitats because of the differences in environmental factors (such as the availability of light or water). Work on their own reserve should help them to explain this.

# What is a plant?

Plants are in a separate kingdom from the animals. The plant kingdom includes algae, mosses and liverworts, ferns, gymnosperms (mainly conifers) and flowering plants.

## Algae

If it's slime it's probably algae. Algae are the simplest members of the plant kingdom. They have no true roots, stems or leaves. Most algae are found in water, particularly in oceans (such as seaweeds) but some are found in soil, on tree trunks, on rock surfaces and in deserts.

They are very important in nature as primary producers of food and also because they fight climate change. They help to remove carbon dioxide from the atmosphere by photosynthesis. It has been estimated that the world's algae remove ten billion tonnes of carbon dioxide a year – more than all the land plants put together.

Algae can be many different colours, but the reds and browns are masking the green chlorophyll that is the chemical of photosynthesis. Sometimes there can be explosions in the population of algae, causing thick green slime in garden ponds and lakes or 'red tides' in the sea. These explosions – or eutrophications – occur when human sewage, fertilisers and detergents – all of them rich in chemicals like nitrates and phosphates – pollute the sea, encouraging uncontrolled growth.

## Mosses and liverworts

Mosses like the damp. There are about ten thousand sorts of moss, which, together with the liverworts, make a separate group of non-flowering green plants. They flourish best in damp conditions and because they don't have roots, but rather a 'Brillopad' of fibres, they can grow anywhere – even up walls. They reproduce with spores, which are released from pods at the top of stalks. Peat bogs are formed from a mat of dead moss, squashed and soaked.

Liverworts grow in damp places. The body – called the thallus – carries another small plant which produces a capsule containing spores.

## Ferns

Ferns can grow in harsh conditions. They are green plants, usually with lacy fronds instead of leaves. While many are quite small, some can grow into tropical trees. They grow best in shaded, damp soil, forming spores under their fronds which grow into a special sexual stage called a prothallus. Male sex cells from the prothallus swim to female cells and fertilise them. The young fern grows from this fertilised egg. There are ten thousand different ferns in the world.

## Fascinating facts

- In 1998, a red tide of algae in Hong Kong swept onto beaches, choking the gills of fish and suffocating them. This biggest algal bloom in history threatened to cause a major pollution crisis.

- The sloth moves so slowly and takes so little care of itself that algae grow on its fur, helping to camouflage it.

- Mosses and liverworts were once the forests of the Earth, before the flowering plants.

- Dried sphagnum moss was used for surgical dressings in World War One.

- Elfin gold is a luminous moss found growing in some caves.

## Conifers

Christmas trees are conifers. Conifers are plants that carry their seeds in cones. Most are evergreens. Most grow in the northern hemisphere where their needle-shaped leaves help keep in water and resist the cold. They carry two sorts of cones. The male cones produce pollen and this is trapped by the sticky female cones. The seeds are formed in the female cones and are dispersed by the wind.

Conifers do lose needles – as you will have noticed if you look at the brown carpet in a forest. But new pine needles grow all the year round. Many pine trees produce a strong-smelling resin, and it is possible to tell pine trees apart by their smell alone. Each year a pine tree will produce a new circle of branches, and you can estimate the age of a tall tree by counting these coronets. It beats cutting it down and counting the rings…

## Flowering plants

On numbers alone, these are the world's most successful plants – and the living things we are most likely to think of when we are asked to name a plant.

Flowering plants are divided into two groups on the basis of their seeds; but you are most likely to know the difference from their leaves – those with wide leaves and branching veins (the dicotyledons) and those with narrow leaves and parallel veins (the monocotyledons). The dicots have two-part seeds, like beans and peas. The monocots have one-part seeds, like cereals and sweetcorn.

Their staggering success is down to variety and efficient reproduction. Flowering plants grow everywhere, and have even adapted into parasites (like mistletoe) and carnivores (like the sundew).

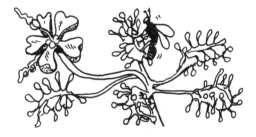

Some have found ways of living together with other living things. Peas, beans and clover plants have lumpy bits on their roots containing bacteria that can provide them with nitrogen – so they can live in poor soil.

Flowering plants produce an infinite variety of fruits, too – large ones like apples and bananas, smaller berries, huge melons and marrows. We eat almost every part of them – celery stems, carrot roots, sprout buds, broccoli flowers, onion bulbs and a huge variety of seeds (peas, beans, maize, rice, wheat) and leaves (greens of every sort). They provide us with herbs and spices, too.

### Trees are flowers, too

Broad-leaved trees are flowering plants, too. Together with the conifers, they provide the tallest living things on Earth. They lose their leaves in winter, so that they can conserve water which they might lose through the leaves' tiny spiracles. Waste products are dumped in the leaves. You see, trees can't go to the loo. Waste products, like acids, have to be dumped somewhere; popping them in falling leaves in autumn loses them for good. This causes the destruction of the chlorophyll in them and it is the chlorophyll that makes leaves green. Its destruction produces the colours we usually see as the leaves 'turn' in the autumn.

Trees make much of the oxygen we breathe. They play a major role in biodiversity – they are a home to many other plants and animals. We use wood in hundreds of ways – from making houses and furniture to making paper. Trees are part of our history and heritage – and trees look good! Scientists have shown that looking at a tree calms you and lowers your heart rate – really!

## Fascinating facts

- The ginkgo tree is a 'living fossil'. It has survived unchanged over millions of years. Dinosaurs probably ate them.

- The coniferous forests of northern Russia cover over a billion hectares. This is the largest forested area in the world.

There are three other kingdoms (apart from the animal kingdom). The fungi – mushrooms and toadstools and tiny yeasts among them – are one. The Protista – tiny living things – are another. The group that includes the bacteria – the monera – is the third.

## Fungi – not plants!

These are the mushrooms and toadstools, as well as a lot of other living things that cause decay and rot. Fungi feed on dead and decaying plants and animals. They are not green – they cannot make their own food, like plants. They produce spores, not seeds. Their structure can spread for miles under the ground.

## Simple life

There is still debate about how to group the simplest forms of life. The plant and animal kingdoms seem fairly clear. More recently, the fungi, since they could not make their own food like the plants, were put in a kingdom of their own. However, other living things always provided a challenge.

The most recent classification divides the simpler things into two groups with unpronounceable names: the prokaryote (which includes the bacteria and the cyanobacteria – or blue-green algae – where the DNA is not contained in a nucleus) and the protoctista (where the DNA is enclosed). This latter includes the rest of the algae up to the biggest seaweeds, and the slime moulds, together with protozoans like the familiar amoeba.

Science is far from a dead or unchanging subject. This classification could – and probably will – be challenged again. It's just as well that the living things most familiar to children – green plants and animals – are in pretty secure groups. But watch this space!

# Plants and their lives

Yes – plants are alive too! Piaget first identified the stages that children move through in their understanding of 'the life concept', and his research would suggest that at the junior school age, movement is equated with life – so that things that appear to move by themselves – including rivers and the Sun – are deemed alive.

If that type of confusion seems improbable, consider the apple you are about to eat for your lunch. You may have difficulty in believing that it is alive – yet it respires using its own food source, excretes waste gases, and could reproduce, given the right conditions for its pips. No wonder that, while all 8- to 11-year-olds appear to agree that plants grow, only 69 per cent of them regard plants as living.

Animals clearly show the seven life processes but plants – which may look dead at some times of the year – show them all, too.

**Nutrition** Green plants can make their own food, but they need that food to grow and live.

**Growth** Plants grow, sometimes very slowly. But a new seedling grows a lot faster than a human baby!

**Reproduction** Plants can produce seeds or spores. Some plants reproduce by growing new plants from special stems or roots.

**Respiration** Plants need oxygen to live, and they produce carbon dioxide. Fortunately for us, they produce a lot of oxygen, too!

**Sensitivity** Plants are sensitive to their surroundings. Climbing bean plants sense a stick, and twine around it.

**Excretion** Plants produce waste products; a little carbon dioxide – and a lot of oxygen.

**Movement** Plants move. Some move quite fast – like mimosa, the sensitive plant that closes its leaves when you touch it. Others move more slowly – like the dandelions that open for the Sun, and close at night.

## Making their own food

Green plants are the only living things able to make their own food. They combine water with carbon dioxide from the air and chlorophyll from the leaves to produce glucose (a type of sugar). This process needs light/energy – usually from the Sun – and is called **photosynthesis**. Plants also need to absorb tiny quantities of mineral salts and other nutrients from the soil and we confuse this process by calling it 'feeding' the plant. Plants don't feed – they are food producers, and the first step in most food chains.

Don't forget that plants also respire, just like us. They don't breathe as such – mechanically drawing air into and expelling it from the body – but they use oxygen in their cells in the process that releases energy from stored foods. At night, they will respire but not photosynthesise. During the day, they are doing both. Fortunately for life on Earth, the amounts of oxygen plants use are exceeded by the amounts they produce. (Hospitals once removed plants from wards at night in case plant respiration took the oxygen from the air and stifled the patients!)

So how does a green plant trap and exploit the energy of sunlight? **The answer is so complex that a Nobel prize was awarded to a scientist who, in 1961, went a long way towards explaining it!**

### The secret of life

So, take a deep breath. Here we go. To start with, photosynthesis takes place in two stages. In the first, sunlight is used to split water into oxygen and hydrogen. This depends upon the ability of a green pigment in plants called chlorophyll to split water molecules. The oxygen is now a waste product – which is a good thing for those of us who favour breathing.

Next, a reaction takes place which doesn't need light. It takes place in a billionth of a second. The hydrogen (actually split into bits by now) is used to convert carbon dioxide into carbohydrates – basic building blocks for sugars, starch and a wide range of materials – including cellulose, the material that plant cell walls are made from. As a result, the plant has food for activity – and also material for growth – both of which we can exploit by eating a cucumber sandwich.

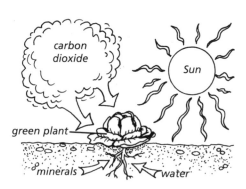

## Why are plants that shape?

To make their food by photosynthesis, plants need to catch the light of the Sun. Their whole structure is aimed at collecting and using as much sunlight as possible.

They have a branching root system that can grip the soil. There is as much tree below the ground as above it (the roots of a tree are roughly the same size and extent as its canopy). They have a strong stem (sometimes a trunk) that can hold the leaves up high – and above the leaves of competitors – and a mathematically-precise leaf pattern.

If you want to see the effectiveness of the leaf pattern, stand under a tree on a sunny day. The leaves are laid out to ensure that even the lower ones make use of the light missed by those above them. The result is a complete shadowing of the ground beneath a mature tree.

### Fascinating facts

- The raffia palm from the islands of the Indian Ocean has the world's largest leaves – 20 metres long.

- Rhubarb and potato leaves are poisonous. So are azaleas, foxgloves and rhododendrons. Yew and laburnum seeds, hyacinth bulbs and mistletoe berries are poisonous, too.

## Plant factories

Most green plants have leaves. Leaves are food factories. They are usually green with chlorophyll, and arranged to catch the Sun. They have veins for transport, and tiny holes to take in and lose gases. In the winter, the leaves may fill with waste products and change colour. A cork layer grows across the base of the leaf, and it falls off.

The flower reproduces the green plant. It usually has both male and female parts. The male pollen is carried by the wind or by insects to another flower. The pollen fertilises the eggs which develop into seeds and which are then dispersed.

## The support structure

The roots anchor and support the plant. Delicate root hairs take in water and some mineral salts. Some roots – like potatoes and carrots – store food. Others bud to form new plants.

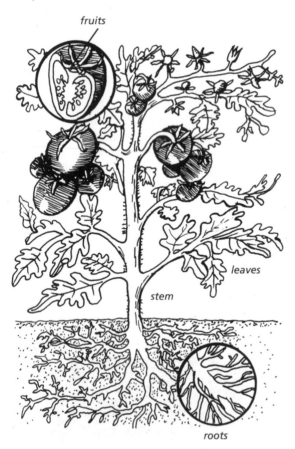

fruits

leaves

stem

roots

The stem supports the leaves and flowers. It may lift them above other plants. The stem contains tubes that carry materials around the plant. Some stems are used to store food. Others touch the ground and bud to form new plants. Green stems can also photosynthesise, like leaves.

## Fascinating facts

- One gram of orchid seeds contains over a million seeds.

- Bamboo plants may live for 100 years before they flower; then they die shortly afterwards.

- The desert holly survives in North American deserts by growing its leaves at an angle. For most of the day, the Sun strikes the leaf edges – avoiding burning.

- The duckweed is the world's smallest flowering plant. It is half a millimetre long.

- 'Athlete's foot' is a fungus that grows on your body – between your toes.

- Lichens are organisms made up of two living things, living together – algae and fungus. The fungus protects the algae in its body, and the algae make food for the fungus by photosynthesis.

## Plants need nutrients

Plants need nutrients to live. But they do not need food like animals. They need simple chemicals in tiny quantities: potassium, phosphorus, nitrogen and others. Plants take these minerals from the soil. And we supply it in 'plant foods' – natural or artificial fertilisers. Plants can grow without these supplements – but deprivation of one of these minerals will show in poor or unusual growth patterns.

## Transport system

Flowering plants have two systems of fine tubes running through them. One set carries materials made in the leaves round the plant. The other set carries water and dissolved minerals from the roots to the leaves. You can see these transport systems in leaves. They are the leaf 'veins'. The water carried to the leaves may be 'transpired' – lost to the atmosphere. This transpiration helps cool the leaves on hot days, and it also plays its part in the water cycle.

## How do they grow?

Children may imagine that plants grow because they swell – rather like a balloon. This is true, in part, of plants. Individual cells fill with water and swell to produce the rapid elongation of shoots and roots. But most growth is by cell division – the splitting of cells to increase the number – but not the volume – of cells. The subsequent swelling of the new cells leads to permanent growth. Some of these new cells, of course, will become specialised structures – flowers, fruits, new leaves.

Plants will grow in the dark (most seeds germinate underground) but they are dependent upon their food reserves if they have no sunlight to use. They grow long and straggly and lose their green colour. This, incidentally, is called 'etiolation'. Plants grown in the cupboard look like this. Since they are longer, children may think that they are 'better' than shorter, healthier plants on the windowsill. We're the same – we will grow in the dark (not necessarily long and straggly) but we'd certainly lose our colour!

### Fascinating facts

- Fresh fruit is alive. It respires, taking in oxygen and giving out carbon dioxide. It reproduces – its seeds can grow into new plants.

- In the spring, you can hear the water rushing up large trees by putting a stethoscope to the trunk.

- An adult elephant needs 140kg of plant food every day.

## How are plants and animals different?

Both animals and green plants need oxygen to live. Both produce carbon dioxide gas. But in sunlight, green plants can take carbon dioxide and combine it with water, making the oxygen both will need.

The arrows in the pictures below show the gases going into and coming from animals and green plants – in the day, and at night. Each arrow stands for a gas. Notice that some arrows are larger than others, representing different amounts.

So plants respire all the time. But they photosynthesise during daylight hours, producing the oxygen we need to breathe – and light our fires, run our transport systems, and do the thousand and one things we do that demand a release of energy. It's a good thing the plants are around; without them we would quickly run out of oxygen. Because all we do is respire – use the oxygen up – we are totally dependent on plants for life itself.

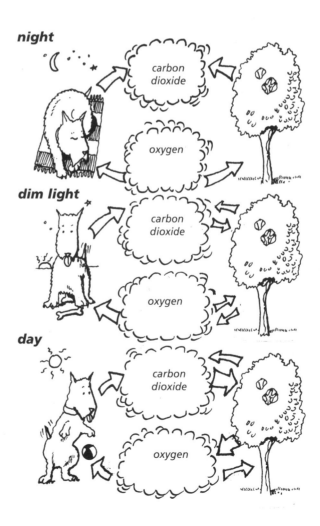

## Plants and climate change

Plants 'lock up' the Sun's energy in themselves. Burning plants – or plant products like coal – releases that energy. But it also releases a waste product – carbon dioxide – that adds to the 'blanket' surrounding the Earth. When we burn coal, we are releasing carbon dioxide that has been locked up for millions of years. When we destroy the rainforests, we are releasing carbon dioxide faster than the remaining trees can absorb it. This waste gas adds to the blanket around the Earth.

This imbalance is thickening the blanket. It acts like greenhouse glass. The heat can get in, but most of it can't get out. The result is the increasing temperature of the Earth, which many scientists suspect is due to our burning of fossil fuels. Unless we achieve a balance between the production of greenhouse gases and their absorption, we face increasing temperatures, the melting of the icecaps and the flooding of low-lying land. Plants matter – all of them. And there is a huge variety, including carnivores…

## Carnivorous plants

Some plants grow in very poor soils – in bogs and marshes. These soils are short of vital minerals. Therefore the plants need another source of minerals. They trap and kill animals, taking the minerals from the bodies of insects, tiny water animals and even baby frogs.

- The sundew is a plant with sticky tentacles. Insects stick to the leaf, which slowly curls over to surround them.
- The Venus flytrap has a hinged leaf covered in sensitive 'trigger hairs'. When an insect touches the hairs, the leaf snaps shut.

- The bladderwort lives in water. It sucks in tiny creatures that touch its trigger hairs. Water rushes into the plant's bladders, carrying animals with it.
- The pitcher-plant has bottle-shaped leaves. Insects fall into the pitcher and are absorbed. Carnivorous crab spiders spread webs across the mouth of the pitcher and steal the plant's prey.

## Plant products

Plants give us many of the products we use every day. Apart from food, these include medicines, like aspirin which first came from the bark of willow trees. Medicines from rainforest plants include cocaine which numbs your mouth at the dentist, quinine which we use to treat malaria and senna which we use to treat constipation. Smells and flavours, like nutmeg on puddings, cloves in bread sauce, cinnamon in drinks and vanilla in icecream are all from rainforest plants. Furniture is made from special and beautiful woods like mahogany, teak and sapele which are grown in the rainforests. Balsa for models is a rainforest wood.

Clothes are made from plant products like cotton and linen. There are other uses, too. Seaweed extract – or carrageen – is used to thicken ice creams. You may find carrageen in soft drinks, toothpaste and even explosives. It helps keep a good head on a glass of beer.

## Fascinating facts

- The world's largest living thing is almost certainly a fungus. Fungi can grow – under the ground – for kilometres.

- Some bacteria can 'eat' stone. They produce sulphuric acid which eats into the stone, making carbon dioxide that they live on.

- The scientist Lord Kelvin first suggested in the 19th century that life may have come to Earth from another planet by 'seeding' with spores, bacteria and micro-organisms.

- Chlorophyll, the green pigment in leaves, is very like the haemoglobin in blood. When the importance of chlorophyll in photosynthesis was first discovered, it was thought to be a miracle material. It was even put into toothpaste. Sadly, it's only good at the one trick.

# Activities

## Level One

Show the children a cut flower – with some leaves – and the nearest type (and best) of artificial flower you can find. Ask them if they can tell which is the real flower. They may need to have touching and smelling suggested to them. Ask them which is alive, and how they know. Children commonly point out similarities rather than differences, so draw their attention to the points that are not obvious. A flower will grow, produce seeds, wilt and die. A flower has needs – water and light – and uses gases from the air – though we can't see that.

Ask the children to record what happens to the real flower. Lay the foundations for understanding that flowering plants produce seeds.

## Level Two

Record the differences between a plant that is given plant food and one that is not. But make it clear that both grow; the plant food only helps accelerate the growth.

Demonstrate a green plant's need for light. Germinate some cress seeds on the windowsill. Notice how the shoots bend towards the window. Show the children how they are seeking the light. You can correct the bend by putting a plastic mirror behind the seeds and equalising the light. (A sheet of silver foil will do.)

## Level Three

Ask the children what plants need to grow. Apart from water and sunlight, there are also invisible gases, but this is a difficult area to explain. Ask the children to name some plant foods, and as each one is listed, say 'And the plant made that using energy from the Sun.'

Conduct experiments with the children to show what happens to plants when they are deprived of either light or water, or both. The children should record what happens.

Ask the children to look around them for plant products – clothes, furniture – and to record how many things 'came from the energy of the Sun'.

## Level Four

Ask children to devise some ways of making plants grow better. Plants grow when they have water, light and air – and they grow better with warmth, too. These are provided in a well-managed greenhouse. You might start by evaluating classroom greenhouse substitutes – what is the result of growing identical plants in the same place, some inside and some outside a propagator? Put a digital or fever strip-type thermometer both inside and outside the propagator, and compare the temperatures.

Does warmth help plants to grow better? Why might that be? Could it be that the food manufacturing takes place faster in the warmer conditions? Record the differences in growth on a line graph.

## Level Five

Cover parts of plant leaves and observe the loss of pigment under the covers. Relate this to the way that plants use pigment called chlorophyll to convert water and oxygen to material for food and growth. Try putting pieces of coloured seaweeds and leaves that are not green in hot water and find out how the colours are washed out, leaving the green chlorophyll.

Begin to record the process of photosynthesis in symbols and words.

# Do plants have babies?

**While many children can accept that animals reproduce sexually, very few – perhaps because they may equate sexual reproduction with copulation – believe that plants reproduce sexually.**

Sexual reproduction involves the combining of genetic material from two parents to produce a new individual. It happens with both plants and animals. Sometimes the product of the process doesn't even look alive. Some children believe that hens' eggs and seeds are not alive, though in changed circumstances either may produce new life – though not, of course, 'breakfast eggs' which are not fertilised.

Research has shown that many children believe that new life is formed from components or parts; new human babies manufactured 'in a mummy's tummy' from bits; chicks assembled from kits of legs, wings, head and body floating around inside the egg.

It's just not like that. All life begins as a single cell – usually the result of combining the cells of two different parents. But there can be reproduction without fertilisation – asexual reproduction and even cloning.

Sexual reproduction has the great advantage that it mixes the characteristics of plants (and animals) and gives them a big stir. But plants can reproduce without sex.

## Crocuses, daffodils, onions and potatoes

These are only four of the plants that reproduce asexually from modified roots of some kind – the first three from bulbs, the potato from a modified root called a tuber.

But you will know this if you have neglected the vegetable rack. Onions and potatoes can set off and start new lives without the need for a flower. Both will sprout and a new plant is produced. The same is true of flowers that grow from bulbs. This is quite a handy strategy if (like many flowers that grow from bulbs) you live in a forest. Having a bulb means that you have the stored energy to flower really early. Even if you produce early flowers (and notice that snowdrops, hyacinths, daffs and crocuses are all spring flowers) you may not be successful in fertilising and spreading your seeds. So a neat fall-back is to have a bulb that you can fill with stored energy all the year, and then try to be the early bird once more. You can even split your bulb, so that the plant reproduces underground.

This is not the only way of reproducing without flowers. Strawberries produce runners; many trees produce suckers. And for hundreds of years, mothers have been embarrassing their children by pinching cuttings from the gardens of strangers and practising the evil art of cloning.

### Fascinating facts

- The world's smallest seeds are from the orchid flower. A million seeds weigh less than one gram.

- We eat the fruits of many plants as food. The avocado fruit is the most nutritious in the world. Avocado fruits contain ten times the energy of a cucumber.

### Cloning

A clone is a living thing taken from another. We have been cloning plants for years – taking a cutting from one plant to grow another. Animals can be made from a single cell, too. The animals that are produced from this cell have the same blueprint – just like identical twins. Dolly the sheep was one of the first animals to be cloned from a single cell. And it is possible to clone humans.

The geranium is a plant with soft, furry leaves. Often, the flowers are red or pink. You can make new plants from an old one. Carefully break off a side branch from the main stem by pulling it downwards. Press your cutting into a small pot of compost or soil. Water it regularly. It will grow roots and eventually become a plant exactly like its parent. You have created a clone!

Life follows a distinct cycle, with birth, growing and reproductive phases, and always ending in death. Understandably, animal metamorphosis – the spectacular life-cycle in which animals undergo huge changes – caterpillar to butterfly, tadpole to frog – catches the imagination. But most animals produce young that resemble the adult – even those that go through partial metamorphosis – a 'nymph' stage.

But plant reproduction can be equally interesting, especially if – like many primary-aged children – you believe that seeds grow in packets!

## So what do plants do?

Flowering plants reproduce with seeds; other plants commonly use spores. Many children have had little experience of harvesting and growing seeds, and few have had the opportunity to see a flowering plant go through its whole life-cycle. They may not be able to recognise the circle that starts and ends with a seed.

Green plants carry flowers, whose sole purpose in life is to ensure that their ovum is fertilised by pollen from another plant, either wind-blown or delivered by insects. Flowering plants produce seeds which are carried away, ensuring that the new plants when they grow do not compete with their parents. The seeds are commonly carried on (strawberry) or inside (apple and pear) fruits. These fruits are often intended to be eaten – which is good news for us and for other animals. The seeds may be discarded, or they may pass through the eater to reach the ground and germinate. Seeds of other fruits – like the tufts of the dandelion – are carried on the wind.

## How plants reproduce

Most green plants have special structures called flowers. Flowers are the reproductive parts of the plant. Flowers are fine examples of biodiversity. There is a huge range of types, in many colours, patterns and shapes. But they all have the same aim – the continuation of the species.

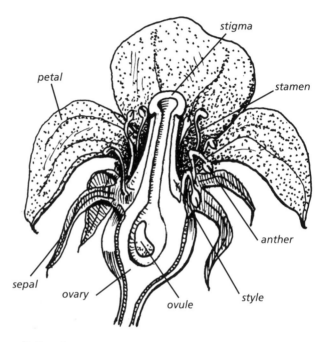

### Pollination

Male and female plant cells must be brought together for seeds to form. This process is called pollination. The male stamens produce pollen in their anthers. The pollen is carried to another flower by the wind or by insects. When the pollen grain reaches the stigma of another flower, it grows a pollen tube down to the female ovule. The ovule is fertilised and forms a seed. The ovary becomes a fruit – the container of the seed.

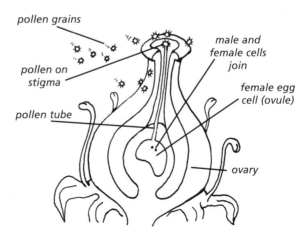

*A pollen grain lands on the stigma and the pollen tube grows down the style.*

Pollen is amazing stuff. This fine powder that is such a nuisance to hayfever sufferers is not just dust. Each particle is beautifully patterned so that its delicate projections can catch and hold an insect, or so that it can be easily blown to another flower. Like golf balls, the dimples on a pollen grain can make it fly better.

## Seed dispersal

If new plants grew all around their parents, they would crowd them out. They would take the precious sunshine, soil and water. So parent plants disperse their seeds as far away as possible. They do this in many different ways. Seeds can't walk. So the plants find other ways of spreading them around.

### In the wind

Dandelion fruits look like tiny parachutes. The seeds can be carried as far as 10km from the parent plant. Sycamore 'helicopters' spiral down from the tree and can be blown great distances. All such plants make maximum use of the wind to carry their seeds great distances.

### On animals

Burrs are hooked fruits that get caught in the fur of passing animals. The animals rub them off, a long way away. (The burrs on the coat of his dog gave an inventor the idea for Velcro – a material covered in tiny hooks that holds onto a mat of fibres.) Hundreds of seeds can be found in the mud on the feet of birds.

## As food

Fruits and berries can be food for birds and animals. The seeds inside pass right through the animal, to be left somewhere new. Even the huge seed of the avocado is swallowed by the resplendent quetzal bird. Fortunately for him (or her), the nut doesn't pass right through but is regurgitated, usually some way from the tree. Bird and tree are dependent on each other.

Animals collect and bury nuts for winter food. They don't find all their nut stores, and some are left to grow. Squirrels are useful little amnesiacs – carrying acorns away from the tree and burying them in subsequently forgotten caches.

### On water

Water plants launch their seeds into rivers and streams. Coconuts, which have a thick, fibrous coat round the familiar nut, float along the shores of tropical islands. Most of these seeds will not find a place to grow. Those that do may not be in the best place. Very few will grow to produce seeds themselves. This is why plants make so many seeds.

## Fascinating facts

- The stapelia flower makes a smell like rotting meat. Female flies are attracted to it by its smell, laying their eggs on petals that resemble dead animals. They take away the plant's pollen.

- Open sesame! Sesame seeds burst open when they ripen.

### Other methods

Some plants, such as peas, have fruits that twist and dry as they ripen. These suddenly burst open and shoot out the seeds they contain.

Lupin seeds are propelled by their twisting pods.

Conkers, from the horse chestnut tree, fall to the ground and the shells split open so that the nut inside rolls away.

When the flower of the poppy has died, it leaves behind a dried seed pod which has holes in it just like a pepper pot. The wind blows the pod and the seeds are shaken out through the holes.

*poppy seed head*

No means of dispersal exists for maize or sweetcorn seeds. They can only have been spread by human intervention. The cobs must have been cut; the seeds harvested and scattered. This would suggest that maize is one of the earliest cultivated crops. How else would it find new places to live?

### Germination

Germination is when a new plant grows from a seed. Seeds germinate in the right conditions – they need warmth and moisture. At first, the plant grows using a food store in the seed. As the food store is used up, the plant begins to make its own food through photosynthesis. Some plants use parts of the seed as their first leaves.

You will remember that there are two sorts of flowering plants – the broad-leaved ones with branching veins (the dicots) and the narrow-leaved ones with parallel veins (the monocots). They have different seeds – and their different seeds behave in different ways.

### Two ways of germinating

The maize seed is a monocot seed. (Monocotyledon means 'one seed leaf', and that's all it's got.) You will be familiar with the maize seed, either because you have chewed it off the cob or because you took unfair advantage of it, dropping it into very hot fat so that the water inside suddenly became steam and exploded it to make popcorn. In maize seeds, the seed leaf stays under the ground. The shoot uses its stored energy (unless you ate it as popcorn) to power up out of the ground.

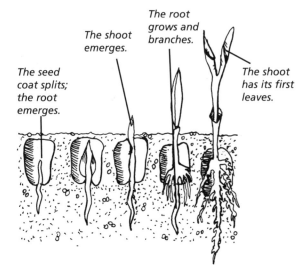

*The root grows and branches.*

*The shoot emerges.*

*The seed coat splits; the root emerges.*

*The shoot has its first leaves.*

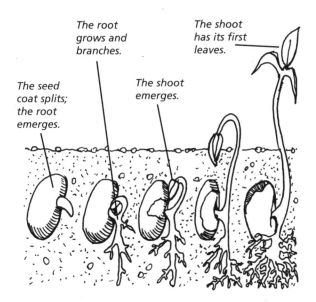

*The root grows and branches.*

*The shoot has its first leaves.*

*The seed coat splits; the root emerges.*

*The shoot emerges.*

## Fascinating facts

- Arctic lupin plants grew from 10,000-year-old seeds found frozen in the Canadian Yukon.

- The cars in the high speed Indianapolis 500 race all run on ethanol fuel from plants.

- Banyan trees develop extra trunks that mean that a single tree can be 600 metres around. A single tree in Sri Lanka has 3,300 trunks.

The bean seed is a dicot. The two seed leaves, having started the whole germination thing, may get hauled up out of the ground to form the first real leaves, turning green and photosynthesising like crazy. Later leaves take over the job as the plant grows.

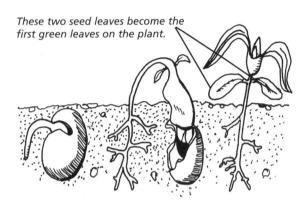

These two seed leaves become the first green leaves on the plant.

Other plants leave all the seeds in the soil. But they quickly grow leaves when they grow into the light. Seeds look dead. But they are alive, although they are living very slowly. They are dormant.

The soil is important, of course, but its main function is to anchor the plant and provide a water source through the roots. The germinating seedling needs food. It has to find sunlight as soon as possible. Fortunately, it is provided with a starter pack. Most seeds contain a food store for initial germination. It's this food store that we exploit when we eat beans, peas and other pulses. But a germinating seed quickly grows a root to draw water and nutrients from the soil.

It's perfectly possible for plants to grow with water and light alone in soil-less conditions. This is called hydroponics. Plants can be grown in sand or gravel – but nutrients must be added.

## Sustainable woodlands

Trees take many years to grow and a few seconds to cut down. People need trees for fuel and this can lead to tree felling on a huge scale. India is the place where most of the world's tropical hardwood grows. The population of India will soon be a billion people, and four of every five trees they cut down are burned for cooking and heating.

Sustainable woodlands and forests are places where each tree burned down is replaced with a new, young tree. Coppicing provides wood for fuel. Trees like willow and poplar are cut short every year and the wood is used for fuel. The roots remain, and new wood grows the next year.

By replacing or coppicing the trees we harvest, we ensure that there will be trees for future generations.

Trees don't just provide oxygen, fruit and wood. They help put a lot of water back into the atmosphere; and their roots bind the soil together. No trees can mean a landslide.

## Fascinating facts

- Only one tree in a hundred is cut for commercial purposes. The rest are cut to clear land, to burn or because they are in our way.

- We are only replacing one tree for every ten we cut down.

- It's the clear sunlight that produces the wonderful colours of the North American 'fall'. First, clear sunny days result in the production of a red pigment called anthocyanin in the leaves. Then the clear, cloud-free autumn air means that we see these colours very sharply.

- Some bristlecone trees in America are over 4,600 years old.

- The tallest living tree is a redwood in a Californian National Park – (111 metres). But an Australian eucalyptus topped that. It was measured in 1872 at 152 metres.

- The annual growth of a tree gives the rings inside the trunk. The wide, light ring is the fast growth of spring and summer; the narrow dark ring is the slow growth of winter. It is possible to age the tree from the rings.

- The earliest ginkgo trees appeared 160 million years ago.

# Activities

## Level One

Show the children some seeds. Ask where they came from. They may have come from a packet, but where did they come from before that? Seeds are made by plants, and are often presented in a carrier called a fruit. You could have some familiar fruits available – apple, grape, orange, tomato – and show how they contain seeds. (We have tricked some plants into producing seedless fruits.) Are seeds alive? They certainly are; they only need a change in conditions – water and warmth – to prove it.

Plant some of the seeds. Grow some seedlings.

## Level Two

Growing plants from seed is easy enough. Taking them through the complete life-cycle – from seed to seed – is difficult, since it takes time. Perhaps the best approach is to grow tomato plants from seeds taken from a cut tomato. Wash and dry the seeds and store them until you need to use them, then plant them in compost, 'feed' them with liquid tomato manure and pinch out side shoots to accelerate growth and flowering. A sunny windowsill will do, but keep the compost moist and support the growing plant. Plants started around Easter should fruit by the end of the summer term.

Look at the range of seeds. Introduce the idea that the whole point of a seed is to travel – to hitch a lift that will take the seed somewhere else to start a new life where it doesn't compete with its parents! Simple card spinners, cut and folded, will carry a Blu-tack 'seed' slowly to the ground. Launched outside – in a bit of wind – they will travel outwards as well as down, illustrating the flight of fruits like the sycamore wing and the lime key.

## Level Three

Develop life-cycle understanding. Give the children some paper plates or paper with a large circle drawn on it and ask them to draw a complete life-cycle – flower to flower – around the ring. If this is too difficult, provide them with pictures of the steps – flower, seed, seedling, small plant, large plant, flowering plant again – and ask them to order and glue them into the ring. Does it matter where they

start? Record the life-cycles of different plants, using secondary sources.

Try growing plants for a set date. If you make this date reasonable and attainable, it can add a bit of spice to the business of plant growing. Practical examples include growing flowers to bloom around Mother's Day, growing lettuces for sale at a summer fair and growing cress so that you can eat cress sandwiches in two weeks' time.

## Level Four

What are the children's own questions about seeds? Putting aside the uninvestigable – which is the biggest, the smallest and so on – you may be presented with some which could be tested. If not, you might encourage them with hints and leading questions.

Possibilities are: If we planted these seeds, which would be the first to germinate? (Either use the same seeds, but vary the conditions, or seeds from different plants for comparison.) Do the biggest seeds make the biggest plants? (Rather inconclusive, this – how long do you wait to see which is the 'biggest plant'? – but there are nice examples of seed sizes – conkers without the prickly case are seeds, and are clearly much bigger than poppy seeds.)

## Level Five

Every gardener knows that clearing a patch of land is inviting new weed growth; but where do these new plants come from? Try clearing a test patch of ground. Watch it over the next few weeks. What grows? Probably you didn't clear all the seeds and tiny plants but many of them will have arrived – sometimes floating or flying in. A less strenuous approach is to fill a seed tray with potting compost, leave it out and see what grows. This will take longer than a patch of soil – the compost will be sterile – but you can still anticipate some new plants in time.

Use this experiment to make sure the children can describe the main functions of the different parts of a plant – leaves, stem, roots, stamen and so on.

# Is an insect an animal?

There are about a million different kinds of animals. Many have common names, such as rabbit or robin, but, of course, they have different common names in other languages. Names for the same living thing vary in different cultures. The bird that Americans call a robin is different from the one people in Britain call a robin. And American jack rabbits do not dig burrows.

In the 1700s a Swedish scientist called Carl von Linné (or Carolus Linnaeus) invented a system to make sense of the way scientists group and name living things. The system is based on how similar and different living things are. He placed them in groups.

## The classification system

### Kingdoms

All living things in a group look similar or have things in common. The largest groups are called **kingdoms**. Plants form one kingdom; animals form a separate kingdom. The smallest groups are **species** – cows, tigers, oak trees are all examples of species. In between are **phyla** or divisions, classes, orders, families and genera.

### Phyla

Animals are grouped into phyla. **Vertebrates** include all the animals that have a backbone and they form one phylum. There are over 20 other phyla of animals. They all have no backbones and together are known as **invertebrates**.

### Classes

Phyla are divided into classes. There are seven classes of vertebrates – mammals, birds, reptiles, amphibians and three classes of fish.

### Orders

Classes are divided into orders. Carnivores (meat-eaters), whales, seals and walruses, and elephants are four of the nine orders of mammals.

### Families

Orders are divided into families. Cats, weasels, bears and dogs are four of the seven families of carnivores.

### Genera

Families are divided into genera. The cat family includes the genus Panthera – that is the big cats such as tigers, lions and cheetahs – and the genus Felis – the cats that purr rather than roar.

### Species

Finally, genera are divided into species. Species are unique. Members of a species are a bit like the aristocracy; they breed with one another but (in normal circumstances) they can't breed with anyone else!

## Fascinating facts

- Dogs are part of an order – a group – that includes other carnivores – bears and cats. Dogs, foxes and wolves all belong to the same family; there are several species of fox, and they cannot breed with one another.

- There are over 100,000 species of mollusc, from slugs to octopuses. The giant clam has a shell over 100cm across.

- Sponges are the most primitive multi-celled animals of all. They eat but cannot move around. They feed by filtering food from the water.

## Two names

Linnaeus gave each species a two-part name. The two parts work like your surname and first name. They tell you which genus and species each living thing is. The ancient language of Latin is used for the names. This is so that everyone can understand them, no matter which language they normally speak. For example, the Latin name for a tiger is *Panthera tigris*. The genus is *Panthera* and the species is *tigris*. The scientific names are given group names first. Think of some children's names and reverse them: Smith, Sharon, for example. Notice that the first, or generic, name always has a capital letter. The specific name always has a lower case initial letter. For example, 'Homo sapiens'.

## Putting them in groups

Animals are divided into two groups on the basis of their possession of a backbone; backboned (vertebrate) and without a backbone (invertebrate). Aristotle made the first recorded classification of plants and animals, dividing living things into animals and protozoans – which moved – and every kind of plant, alga and fungus – which didn't. Linnaeus produced the structure of a five-kingdom classification – plants, animals, fungi, single-celled algae and Protista, and bacteria. He went on to classify and relate the plants, using their external characteristics; but this approach let him down when he came to classifying animals. The internal structures of animals – and especially whether they have a backbone – are much more important to their family relationships than what they look like.

*With a backbone*

fish

amphibians

birds

reptiles

mammals – including the monotremes

*Without a backbone*

coelenterates

flatworms

roundworms

annelid worms

molluscs

echinoderms

arthropods

There are some living things that don't fit either the animal or the plant kingdom.

- The fungi are a separate group of living creatures, for example, with a branching body that is not green, that cannot make its own food and instead absorbs food from its surroundings.
- Lichens are organisms made up of two living things living together, algae and fungi.
- Bacteria are very simple cells with rigid walls. They can reproduce by dividing in two, as well as producing spores.

## Why are things grouped differently?

Take two fish; one bony fish, a teleost, and one cartilaginous (soft-boned) fish, a shark or elasmobranch. Compare them and you will see why they are grouped differently.

How are they alike? This is easy if you focus on the number of fins, eyes, mouth and so on. But how are they different? There may not be any immediate differences beyond colour, shape and size. Look for differences in the skin, teeth, shape of body and other finer points.

What if we could look inside? Are we likely to find more differences? We could find that they have different bones, for example. In fact there are lots of differences. But both are kinds of fish.

These differences are enough to stop the different types breeding together. So these separate types are unique; and we call them separate **species**. The nice thing is that if you find one, a completely new species can be named after you! So if you found a new species of frog, it would be called – not Rana temporaria (the common frog) but Rana _____ (insert your name here)!

### Fascinating facts

- The smallest mammal in the world is the bumblebee bat. It weighs two grams.

- The largest mammal is the blue whale. It can grow over 30 metres long and weigh around 200 tonnes.

- The male giraffe can be 5.5m tall.

## What are the differences?

Looking closely at the teleost and elasmobranch (below), you will see that the differences between the two are huge. They include:

- scales of the bony fish versus teeth on the skin of the shark
- small but numerous teeth of the shark
- single gill flap of the bony teleost versus multiple gills of the elasmobranch
- one has bony skeleton, the other a skeleton of rubbery cartilage.

These are big differences. These are not of the same species. They are not even in the same small group. But they are both fish.

## Branching keys

There are different ways of finding out the name of a plant or animal that is new to you. One is to read descriptions of different living things, and see if they match the criteria. Has that bird in the garden a brown head, a red breast or white flashes on the wings? Another is to match it by picture. Many of us will look through the bird book and see if we can find something similar. 'It looks a bit like this. No, it hasn't got a beak like that. Maybe it's this one?' You are helped if you have seen something similar before. It may be very like other finches – or similar to a pigeon. But all these systems are very hit-and-miss. The best way of making an identification is to use a classification – or branching key.

By answering a series of questions, you narrow down your unknown until it is firmly identified. Branching keys for all the wild flowers you are likely to find in the UK tend to run over several pages – and get into complex structural questions – but a small key of the invertebrates in your school garden is quite easy to use, and also is a good exercise for children – whether they are using one, or constructing one.

The idea is to ask questions that split the unknowns into smaller and smaller groups. Take an orange, an apple and a banana – actually not a bad exercise for younger children. Several questions are possible – but the first might be 'Is it round?' The orange and the apple are – but the banana is not. The first question can, sometimes, identify something. Now we have two remaining items to classify, and the next question might be 'Is it green (or red/ yellow)?' That divides the two and identifies each.

Similar keys for plants and animals make it easy to name them. Opposite is a basic identification key that helps with identification and classification of vertebrate animals. Some animals can turn up in more than one category – as mammals do here. It won't cover every living thing but it is a useful tool for children to begin to learn about classifying animals.

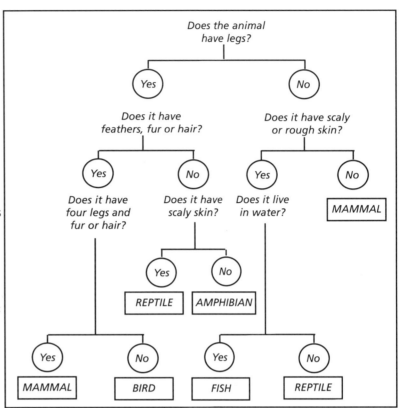

# Vertebrates

### Mammals

There are about 4,000 different kinds of mammal, including mice, elephants, deer, whales and humans. They live in most places in the world, from the icy wastes of the Arctic to the hot deserts of Africa. They even live in the oceans. Mammals have two main things in common that make them different from other animals – they have fur or hair and the females produce milk to feed their young.

Mammals give birth to their young alive, and they suckle them on milk. This new life is formed when a male's sperm joins with a female's egg. With mammals this happens inside the female's body. The female also has a special organ, called the womb, where the fertilised egg or eggs grow and develop into new individuals. Most mammals give birth to babies that are fully formed. Marsupials are mammals whose babies are born when they are only partly formed. The baby climbs into a special pouch on the mother's front or back and stays there, drinking her milk, until it is fully formed. The best-known is the baby kangaroo!

All female mammals have special glands that make milk to feed their newborn babies. For a while, the babies need no other food. The babies need to be looked after by their mothers, and often by their fathers too, until they are old enough to look after themselves. How long this takes depends on the kind of animal. During this time, the young mammals learn how to hunt and survive as adults.

Some mammals live in groups. These groups are called herds, colonies, packs or other special names. Cows, zebra, deer and rabbits are large, plant-eating animals that live in herds. Meat-eating lions and wolves also live in groups. Tigers and otters are just two of the mammals that live and hunt on their own. The following names, or collective nouns, were mostly devised by an inventive nun who felt that 'herd' and 'troop' were a bit dull for the more interesting groups of animals. Using her imagination, she proposed a shrewdness of apes, a sloth of bears, a caravan of camels, a skulk of foxes, a leap of leopards, a crash of rhinoceroses, a pod of seals and a rout of zebra.

Whether the mammal lives in a group or on its own, it has to find a mate in order to reproduce and continue the life-cycle. Sometimes a male and female pair will stay together to look after the young, and sometimes the male leaves the female to look after the young on her own. Females often find a den or sheltered place in which to give birth and look after their babies.

What makes any mammal a mammal is hair. The hair may be unusual – the hedgehog's hair has become spikes, the pangolin's a series of plates – but it is still hair. Whales, dolphins and other marine mammals have some vestigial hairs on their bodies. Some mammals, such as bears and wolves, have thick fur over most of their bodies. Some mammals have much less hair, but if you look closely at your skin you will see that most of it is covered with fine hair. Fur and hair help to keep mammals warm. When it is cold, the hair stands up, trapping a layer of warm air next to the skin. Air is an insulator, retaining body heat.

# Birds

Birds can be found in most parts of the world, in forests, fields and cities – even far out to sea and in the icy Antarctic. What makes birds different from all other animals is their feathers. Not all birds fly – emus and ostriches never leave the ground and penguins have flippers instead of wings. Insects and bats fly as well as birds, but only birds have feathers.

## Feathers and beaks

Feathers are light and airy. Small, fluffy feathers close to the bird's chest help to keep it warm, while the long, flat feathers on its wings and tail help it to fly. The feathers are slightly oily. This means that water runs off them, keeping the bird dry. Birds have to clean their feathers with their beaks to keep them working well (preening).

Birds have hard beaks instead of teeth. The shape of the beak varies depending on the kind of food the bird eats. Birds that eat seeds and nuts have short, strong beaks, while those that catch flies have long thin beaks.

# Reptiles

Reptiles live in most parts of the world, except in very cold places. There are 6,000 different kinds of reptiles. Reptiles include tortoises with shells, snakes with no legs and water-living crocodiles, but they all have dry, scaly skin. Dinosaurs were reptiles and they ruled the Earth for millions of years, until the last ones died out 64 million years ago. The crocodiles are their nearest living relatives, with their front legs smaller than the back ones just like the dinosaurs. Reptiles have backbones and breathe in air. They are all meat-eaters. The families in the main groups of reptiles are turtles and tortoises, crocodiles, lizards and snakes.

## Cold–blooded

Only birds and mammals can make their own heat. Reptiles are cold-blooded. This means that they take in heat from their surroundings. When reptiles become too hot or too cold, their bodies slow down. At night the temperature drops, so, in the morning, each reptile has to warm itself up in the sunshine before it can hunt for food. It controls its temperature by moving from warmth to shade. In very hot places, reptiles burrow underground to stay cool during the hottest part of the day.

# Amphibians

Amphibians are animals that spend part of their life-cycle in water and part on land. They have backbones and are cold-blooded. Frogs are the best-known amphibians, but there are also toads and newts in the UK, and other amphibians in other parts of the world. The axolotl is an extraordinary amphibian that lives in caves in South America. It is a larva that has become sexually mature – rather as if a tadpole could lay eggs. Giving these creatures iodine, which stimulates the thyroid, leads to them losing their gills and becoming a very different-looking adult.

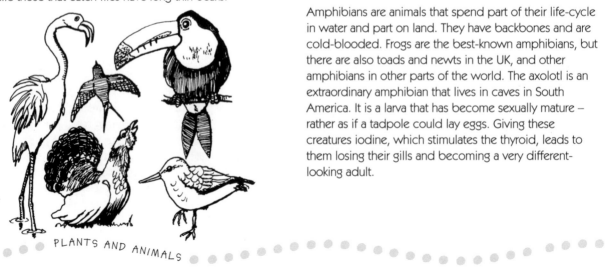

## Fish

Fish are backboned animals that live and breathe in water. They have gills, not lungs, that take in oxygen from the water. Fish have no legs and use their long, streamlined bodies to push them through the water. Instead of limbs they have fins that help them to steer through the water.

Most fish have skeletons made from bones but some, such as sharks, have skeletons made from cartilage. Only bony fishes have skin covered with scales. Most fish are meat-eaters that feed on other fish and animals. They have sharp teeth and a very good sense of smell.

Some fish live alone, but some live in huge groups called shoals. Members of the shoal never bump into each other – they all change direction at the same time to swim around a rock, for example. The shoal swims together until it is attacked by a predator. Then the fish swim off in all directions so that most members of the shoal are bound to survive.

# Invertebrates

Invertebrates are animals that have no backbone. Many, such as shellfish and insects, have a hard skeleton on the outside of their bodies, called an exoskeleton. Some, such as worms and jellyfish, have no skeleton at all. There are more than a million different kinds of invertebrates, whereas there are only about 40,000 vertebrates (animals with backbones). These are some of the main groups or phyla of invertebrates.

## Insects

Insects are a class of invertebrates. They have no backbones, and in fact no bones at all. Insects do have a skeleton that gives their body its shape, but this skeleton is on the outside of their bodies, not inside. It is made of a hard skin, like a suit of armour.

Insects are different from other invertebrates in two main ways. They have six legs and their bodies are divided into three parts – the head, the thorax and the abdomen. The legs grow from the thorax – the middle part of the body. Insects include bees, beetles, flies and all the other kinds of animals with six legs.

Most insects can fly. Many have two pairs of wings but some have only one pair. Beetles, such as ladybirds, have one pair of wings that has become a hard case that protects the lower wings when they are not flying.

Many insects, such as butterflies, go through four stages to become an adult – egg, larva, pupa and adult. (See page 41.)

Locusts – a kind of grasshopper – are one kind of insect that goes through only three stages to adulthood.
- The eggs hatch into nymphs – they look like tiny adults but they have no wings.
- Their skin splits, producing bigger nymphs.
- At the last split the nymph becomes an adult often with wings.

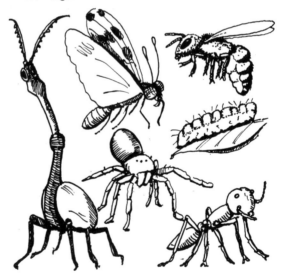

## Sponges

Most sponges live in the sea. They look more like plants than animals. They have no head or limbs and they cannot move from place to place. They attach themselves to rocks and feed by sucking in water.

## Spiny–skinned animals

The scientific name for this group is Echinodermata. It includes sea urchins, starfishes and sea lilies, sea cucumbers and brittle-stars. They all live in the sea and have round symmetrical bodies with spines. The five-sided shape has evolved because it offers no break lines – no places where the animal could snap or tear right across. You see the same idea in five-stud racing car wheels.

## Jellyfish

Jellyfish belong to a group which includes sea anemones and corals. Their bodies are made from soft jelly and they have many tentacles that they use to sting their prey and carry it to their mouths. Coral reefs are made from the shells of millions of tiny polyps. Most of the coral reef is empty shells but on the outside living polyps build new shells and produce more polyps. The sea anemone may look like a flower, but it has deadly tentacles, not petals.

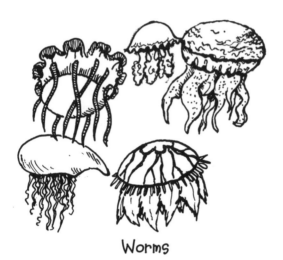

## Worms

There are thousands of different kinds of worms including earthworms which live in soil, roundworms which live inside humans and lugworms which live in sand. Worms are many shapes and sizes, but none has any legs.

## Molluscs

Molluscs have soft bodies and include snails, octopuses and many kinds of shellfish. Many molluscs have a hard shell to protect their soft bodies. Cuttlefish and squid have a shell inside their bodies, but some molluscs, such as slugs, squid and octopuses, have no shells. The shells of molluscs vary in shape. Limpets have cone-shaped shells, while mussels and oysters have two shells joined by a hinge. As a mollusc grows bigger it adds to the shell, making it bigger too.

## Spiders

Spiders (arachnids) have eight legs. I know you know they're not insects but I bet you didn't know that both the spider group and the insect group belong in the same phylum – the arthropods or animals with jointed legs. Spiders eat insects and many weave webs in which to trap their prey. Scorpions are also arachnids.

## Crabs and their relatives

Crabs, lobsters, shrimps and woodlice all belong to the same class of arthropod. They all have hard shells and legs with many joints. Crabs and lobsters also have strong claws to catch their food and defend themselves. As they grow they shed their shells and grow new, larger ones. All shelled animals are faced with this problem.

The soft hermit crab has found a unique way round the challenge of growing. It swaps its empty snail shell for another when it is outgrown. Other crabs have to soften, split and grow a new shell.

## Centipedes and millipedes

Centipedes and millipedes have many legs – anything between 14 and 400. The main difference between them is not the number of legs, but how many there are on each body joint. Centipedes have one pair of legs per joint, and millipedes have two. Centipedes are meat-eaters and feed on insects, earthworms and slugs, while millipedes feed on rotting plants.

## Fascinating facts

- Most flatworms are parasites – living in other animals.

- There are 15,000 different roundworms – some microscopic. Many are parasites.

- The earthworm belongs in the same group of segmented worms as the leeches – 20,000 strong.

- All the echinoderms have five sides. You can see this shape in the starfish, brittle-stars, sea lilies, sea cucumbers and sea urchins.

- There could be ten million types of insect. Nobody knows!

# Activities

## Level One

Using pictures, group animals in different ways. You might use colour or shape. Differences are easy to spot, so look for similarities – having the same number of legs, for example.

## Level Two

Look at the classification of living things into plants and animals. You could use pictures, rather than living things. Put in one or two debatable ones – sessile animals such as barnacles, sponges and sea anemones plus moving plants such as mimosa.

Now try grouping your pictures. Children commonly group by identifying a characteristic – 'This animal has fur,' – and then looking for examples that don't match – 'This animal doesn't.' Try to get them to look at each animal individually rather than make comparisons.

## Level Three

Investigation isn't possible in the area of classification but close observation and decision-making is. Start by asking children to classify seven animals – a fish, an amphibian, a bird, and both a land and a sea mammal such as a whale, and a legged and legless reptile such as a snake. You could use a simple key, leave the questions blank and ask the children to think of some of their own that sort the animals. Look at the example on page 33. Notice that the same type of animal can turn up in two different places.

## Level Four

Using a classification key and some local animals, ask the children to classify them using standard questions.

Where do these living things belong in the animal kingdom?

Ask the children to create a minibeast classification key based on numbers and types of legs and feet – from none (worms), to one (snails), to six (insects), to eight (spiders). How can the children separate two six-legged insects? What questions will they ask?

## Level Five

Use secondary sources to research Carolus Linnaeus and his classification system.

Learn about why the internal parts of animals can be important in classifying living things – for example the different bones of bony and cartilagious fish.

# How long do animals live?

## What is a life-cycle?

The process of birth, growth, reproduction, ageing and death is the animal's life-cycle. The animal may reproduce very simply – by splitting or budding. But large animals can't do this. They need to find ways of reproducing sexually.

When animals reproduce sexually, they make special sex cells, each containing half the information needed to make a new animal. Fertilisation is the process that combines these two cells to make a new one.

Because the male cells – the sperm – need water to swim in, many animals reproduce in water, and amphibians like toads and frogs need to return to the water to breed. But land animals have developed internal fertilisation. The male puts the sperm inside the female's body. Then the new animal develops in a mini-pond – the egg – or inside the mother in the womb. The egg, or the mother's womb, provides a food supply for the developing animal. Eggs are laid and eventually hatch. Mammals are born when the young animal is pushed from the mother's body.

## Lifespans

The expected lifespan of different animals varies widely – with size and type.

### Animals' longest-known life span

| | |
|---|---|
| Adult mayfly | 3 days |
| Mouse | 3 years |
| Guppy | 5 years |
| Large beetles | 5–10 years |
| Swallow | 9 years |
| Coyote | 15 years |
| Giant spider | 20 years |
| Toad | 36 years |
| Lobster | 50 years |
| Crocodile | 60 years |
| Sea anemone | 70 years |
| Elephant | 77 years |
| Blue whale | 80 years |
| Golden eagle | 80 years |
| Sturgeon | 100 years |
| Tortoise | 100–150 years |
| Human | 113 years |

## Life processes

Animals show the seven life processes.

**Nutrition** Animals take in and use nutrients for energy, for growth and to repair and maintain their bodies. These essential nutrients are in the animal's food and almost always originated from a green plant.

**Movement** Animals move and respond to things around them. Plants move too – but not so fast.

**Growth** Animals grow with time, adding to their bodies. This is not expansion – actual material is added to their body.

**Reproduction** Animals produce young to carry on their kind. Almost always, this reproduction is sexual, allowing a deeper dip into the gene pool; but some animals reproduce asexually.

**Respiration** Most animals use oxygen to break down their food, though some animals can break down their food without oxygen.

**Sensitivity** Animals are sensitive to what is happening around them. Most animals have special sense organs that can sense touch, light, sound and often tastes and smells. There are animals that are sensitive to other stimuli – some snakes are sensitive to heat, for example, and can strike their prey in the dark.

**Excretion** Animals get rid of waste products.

**Animals reproduce in different ways. Most lay eggs.**

## Eggs and egg-laying

Most invertebrates lay many eggs. Not many of the animals from these eggs will live long enough to grow old enough to lay eggs themselves. Almost all will die before then – many as the food of other animals.

### Fish

Most fish begin life as an egg laid in a mass of eggs by a female fish and fertilised by a male fish. The mass of eggs floats in the water and many are eaten by fish and other animals. Some fish care for their eggs, but most do not. Sticklebacks defend their nest until the baby fish hatch. Male seahorses protect the eggs in a special pouch. The eggs that survive hatch into tiny fish. Many of these are eaten too. Those that aren't grow bigger and bigger and become adults. In time they lay eggs and the life-cycle begins again.

There are some exceptions to this life-cycle. In some species of shark, the female's eggs are fertilised inside her body and develop into young. They are born after they have hatched. Male seahorses carry the fertilised eggs around in a pouch and look after them until they hatch. The cichlid fish keeps its young in its mouth.

Some kinds of fish live only in the salty water of the sea. Others live in fresh water in lakes and rivers. The salmon is unusual, because it starts life in fresh water and swims downstream to the ocean where it stays for several years before returning to the same stream to breed.

### Amphibians

Amphibians like frogs and toads live on land, but lay their eggs in water. They produce many thousands of tadpoles, but few will grow to be adults. If you are going to be a feckless parent and abandon your offspring to predators and other dangers, then you had better have plenty of them. Huge numbers of eggs are the result of a lack of care, and not the other way around.

The legless tadpoles feed on plants and, later on, other animals. As they grow, they develop legs and their tails shrink back into their bodies. The developing frogs stop breathing through gills and use lungs instead. The new frogs move to land, but come back to the water to breed. A tadpole would die on land; a frog can drown in water.

### Reptiles

The female reptile's eggs are fertilised inside her body. The eggs have a soft, leathery shell. The shell gives the young reptile a mini-pond to develop in. The egg contains food and water stores. With most kinds of reptiles the female then digs a hole in the ground and lays her eggs in it. She covers the eggs and then leaves them to hatch on their own. Many of these eggs and the young reptiles are eaten by other animals. Some snakes and lizards keep the eggs inside their bodies and give birth to fully-formed young, but even then most do not look after their offspring. Only a few lizards and crocodiles stick around to defend their young from attack. When the young that survive grow up, they too find a mate and the life-cycle begins again.

## Fascinating facts

- An ostrich egg is 18cm long and 13cm wide. It contains the food store for the baby ostrich.

- The axolotl is an amphibian that lives in Mexico. It looks like a newt. Axolotls breed to produce new animals just like themselves. But when scientists fed them special food, they changed – they metamorphosed – into an adult animal that had never been seen before.

- Many male reptiles have not one but two penises – which may account for their smug look!

## Birds

A new life is formed when a female's egg is fertilised by a male's sperm. With birds this happens inside the female's body. Birds lay eggs with hard shells. If the egg is fertile, a baby chick can develop. Most birds care for their young – or in the case of cuckoos, arrange foster parents. Because of this care, they can afford to lay fewer eggs than fish or turtles. But there are still dangers to contend with – which is why they frequently over-produce, laying a clutch of eggs rather than the two they need to replace themselves.

Many parent birds build a nest, perhaps from grass, feathers and twigs and the female lays her eggs in the nest one by one. Each egg is protected by a hard shell. One of the parent birds then sits on the eggs to keep them warm as the young birds develop and grow inside the shells. When the chick is ready to hatch, it pecks a hole in the shell and breaks it open.

After hatching, the young birds stay in the nest and their parents bring them food. When they are strong enough, they learn to fly. Birds soon become adults. In less than a year they may have to fly long distances to spend the winter in a warmer country.

When spring comes the adult birds get ready to find a mate. Some birds fly to the cold lands around the Arctic Ocean; others stay where they are. Before long, the females are ready to lay new eggs and the life-cycle begins again.

Many birds make good parents – almost too good – exhausting themselves to feed their young. This is a trait exploited to the full by the cuckoo.

## Egg-laying mammals

When the first duck-billed platypus skin arrived in London in 1799, scientists thought they were being hoaxed. It had the body of a mammal, but the beak and feet of a duck. They searched for the stitches sewing these different bits of animal together. There weren't any. The platypus is a special sort of mammal, a monotreme. It has fur, and feeds its young on milk. Monotremes, like the platypus and the echidna, seem to be stuck in the stage between being a reptile – and so laying eggs – and being a mammal – and so giving birth to its young alive.

The platypus lays leathery eggs. But when its young are born it feeds them on milk. The beak and webbed feet have evolved to suit a life in water very like that of a duck. They are a case of parallel evolution – the same pressures giving rise to the same structures.

## Metamorphosis

Many baby animals do not resemble their parents. The familiar examples of this are the tadpole and frog, or the caterpillar and butterfly. But there are many other cases – the larvae of crabs and sea urchins, for example, where the immature animal has no resemblance to the adult.

The larval stage achieves a particular purpose; the caterpillar is an eating and growing machine and the barnacle larva seeks out new places to live. Not all creatures undergo this complete metamorphosis. Some, like grasshoppers, have young which are similar to the adults, but wingless. Their tiny wings develop with each step through the life-cycle.

## Fascinating facts

- Albatross mate for life. The male will guard the eggs, while the female searches for food. This puts them at greater risk – especially from fishing nets – and leaves many lonely widower albatross.

- The divorce rate among swans is less than 1 per cent.

- Male pied flycatchers are natural bigamists. Having mated, they set off to find another mate, splitting themselves between the two.

Often these animals live in a different way from their parents and sometimes in a different place. They are adapted to this different life.

Butterflies and moths lay eggs which hatch into caterpillars. Caterpillars have no wings, and cannot reproduce. They are eating machines, chomping their way through leaves and growing. As they grow, they split their skins and a new caterpillar emerges. When they split their skin for the last time, they have become a pupa or chrysalis. Inside the pupa, the body parts become liquid. They reassemble themselves as an adult butterfly with wings. The adult may do very little eating. Its job is to fly and to mate. Female butterflies lay eggs, and new caterpillars hatch out.

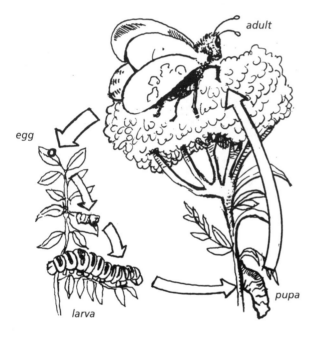

egg

adult

larva

pupa

## Born alive

Mammals and a few other animals give birth to their young alive. The mini-pond that the baby develops in is inside the mother. Mammals cannot have many babies because the mother could not carry them all around. But the developing baby is safer inside the mother and mammals care for the baby once it is born. Mother mammals feed their babies on milk.

Because mammal eggs need to be fertilised inside the mother, mammals have special breeding and mating behaviour and fathers often share in caring for the baby. Elephants even have 'aunts' who help the mother to protect the new baby. The mother elephant has been pregnant for 20 months and the new baby needs special care. But this care from mammals is usually successful, which is why mammals have fewer young than other

animals. Only those that are a reluctant part of the food chain – like rabbits – reproduce in large numbers. Different mammals have different gestation or pregnancy periods.

### Animals' length of pregnancy

| | |
|---|---|
| House mouse | 19 days |
| Chimpanzee | 237 days |
| Camel | 406 days |
| Rhinoceros | 560 days |
| Indian elephant | 624 days |
| Human | 266 days |

## Good parents

Woodlice carry their young with them, under their shells. It is hard to observe their undersides, but some magnifiers, with a built-in mirror, can help you do this. You can see the young clinging to their legs.

Commonly, animals that are born underground or in nests (rabbits, mice) are born immature and have long dependency periods. Animals more exposed to predators – those born on open plains, for example (horses, antelope) – achieve quick independence. That's why a new foal is on its (shaky) legs in minutes.

## Staying alive

Once born – whichever way – the next hurdle is to stay alive! To do this animals need to:
• eat
• keep warm
• evade hunters.

## Food

Animals need food for energy and they release that energy by a cellular process called respiration. (It mustn't be forgotten that plants respire, too. They do not produce food as a selfless activity to support the animal kingdom – see Chapter 2.) Respiration, and the release of energy from food, requires oxygen. Animals are unable to store oxygen and it is the need to regularly renew oxygen stores that leads them to breathe in different ways – through breathing tubes (insects); through gills (fish and young amphibians); through their skin and the lining of their mouths (frogs); or with lungs (reptiles, birds and mammals).

This process releases the energy needed for life. Animals need to maintain this process to survive. This makes the finding and ingesting of food an imperative for every animal on Earth.

## Heat

Living things function because of chemical reactions in their bodies and these chemical reactions will run faster and more efficiently in warmer conditions. Cold-blooded animals become less active in cold conditions – or may artificially boost their body temperature by basking in the Sun. Their body temperature varies with their environment.

Mammals and birds maintain their body temperature, as if they had a thermostat. Since these 'warm-blooded' animals need to maintain these temperatures, they are affected by seasonal change. They may stay active throughout the cold conditions, evade them by going somewhere warmer (migration) or become inactive for weeks at a time (hibernation).

## Fascinating facts

• Mating is a risky business for some male spiders, who risk being eaten by the female. They may tie her down during mating or hold her mouth shut, or distract her with an edible gift.

• A male penguin incubates the single egg laid by the female on its feet in temperatures of –20°C and winds of 200km/hr. He fasts for over 100 days, losing almost half his body weight. The female returns to complete the last few days of the task while the male goes off to feed.

• The grunion is a sea fish that lays its eggs at high tide. The females allow themselves to be swept ashore and stranded, where they lay their eggs and wait to be swept back out to sea. Then the males are swept ashore to fertilise them, and finally another high tide disturbs the eggs and releases the young fish.

## Run or hide – or fight back.

Animals have a variety of ways of evading their predators. They might be able, more often than not, to outrun them – as in the case of the hare escaping the fox. But if they can't, then what other tricks do they have up their sleeves? There is camouflage, where the animal changes in some way to match its surroundings, such as the changing colour of the chameleon and the stick insect who looks just like the twig he is sitting on.

But some animals need have no fear of enemies because they are so unpleasant-tasting, or poisonous, that they can be vividly-coloured, advertising their unpleasantness. A bright red ladybird tastes disgusting to a bird, presumably. Many spiders and scorpions have a deadly bite or sting, and some tarantulas are happy to stand well back and fire irritating hairs at their enemy.

# Activities

## Level One

Using pictures, match animal offspring to the parents. Recognise that some young animals may not resemble their parents.

Understand the idea of life-cycles – and begin to draw them.

## Level Two

Look at the life-cycles where metamorphosis takes place – where animals change as they move through their life-cycle. Record not just the ordinary ones – butterflies, frogs – but also toads, dragonflies and moths.

Keep some classroom examples of metamorphosing animals. Mealworms are ideal. See butterflies emerge from pupae or tadpoles become frogs. Record the changes as a life-cycle diary.

## Level Three

Tadpoles are traditional classroom animals, to the point where numbers have been in danger. Keep very few – a clump of eggs the size of a tennis ball contains about 350 eggs. You need a tank holding 100 litres of water for this number. Even then, an air pump is recommended. Use a chlorine-removing chemical (Haloex or Tetrasafe) and add natural salts (Pondsal) from an aquarium shop to the water. Do not change the temperature of the tadpoles suddenly; add them slowly. Change the treated water weekly. Feed the tadpoles as freshwater fish until they reach the young adult stage, when they should be returned to the pond. At this stage they drown unless they can get out of the water onto a rock and they start to be carnivorous. This makes it impractical to keep them longer.

Record the changes. Note that contrary to popular belief, the tail of a tadpole does not drop off but is absorbed – and that the hind legs grow before the front ones.

## Level Four

Find out about mammalian birth – and nurture of the young. Use secondary sources to find out more about how mammals and birds care for their young.

Make comparisons of animals that are born in dens and tunnels (immature, dependent, sometimes blind) and those that are born in open countryside (mature, active, able to fight or run).

## Level Five

Use secondary sources to understand sexual reproduction in animals. Look at videos, books or the Internet for examples of animal reproduction. Ask the children to compare numbers of offspring and parental care. Why does increased parental care mean that you can have fewer offspring? Compare animal and plant reproduction. How are they alike? How do they differ?

# There's no place like home

A habitat is a plant or animal's address. It is the place that provides them with the needs of life – food, shelter, a mate and somewhere to dump their waste.

The more demanding the habitat, the more animals and plants have to adapt to live there. It's tough being a plant in a desert, or an animal among the ice. So plants and animals have devised many ingenious survival structures and techniques. Penguins and humming-birds, elephants and pygmy mice, sharks and sticklebacks are all adapted to where they live, and these habitats can be both varied and challenging – and also changing all the time.

## Water habitats

Many plants and animals are adapted to living in water. The plants grip strongly to stop them from being swept away. The animals swim strongly, using webbed feet, to stop them from being swept away. These are adaptations to living in water. Many mammals live in water – voles, otters, mink – and the world's largest rodent – the capybara. Pond skaters, whirligig water beetles and insect larvae live on the surface of a pond. More beetles like water boatmen live in mid-water, with tadpoles and fish. Pond snails, nymphs and larvae live among the waterweeds. Worms and leeches live on the bottom.

### Ponds

A pond is a small habitat with its own plant and animal population. When it is in balance, the water is clear and the living things thrive.

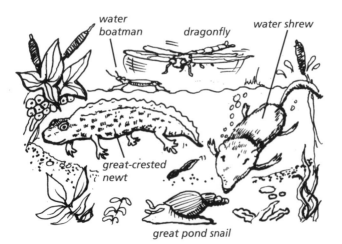

water boatman    dragonfly    water shrew

great-crested newt

great pond snail

### Fascinating facts

- The salt lakes of the USA are home to birds living on their banks – pelicans, herons, cormorants, terns and gulls. The water can be as much as 30 per cent salt.

- In the deepest seas, life survives without light. Mussels in the Gulf of Mexico live off salt deposits and methane gas seeping through the ocean floor.

Plants and animals living in the pond can survive freezing temperatures – ice conveniently forms on top of a pond so that life can continue undisturbed underneath. (In garden ponds the ice should be broken or the fish can die of gas poisoning.) Many living things can also survive the pond drying up. But some cannot, either making their way to new ponds or dying in their changed habitat.

Life begins in new ponds without human help. A study of the feet of water birds showed that they carry seeds, eggs and even active living things from place to place on them. They are the immigration vessels that bring new life.

### Rivers

If you want to live in a river or a stream, you have to either get a good grip on things or be a good swimmer. This is true in every part of the world. An otter living in Suffolk is very like a crocodile living in Miami. True, one is a mammal and the other a reptile, but both have a long, flattened body they use for swimming, webbed feet and a nose and ears that can close under the water. Both are good swimmers. The alternative is to hang on.

Good hangers-on include the lamprey – a fish with a sucker-shaped mouth – and the catfish of South America that also has toothed fins that can be used to grab rocks.

A long, smooth shape can ease the flow of water around the body of river animals, so that they have to make less effort just to stay in one place; you can see this same shape in the long waterweeds that sway in the current.

## Canals and streams

A canal is an artificial stream and many of the same habitat conditions apply as you find in actual streams. But canals are also a managed habitat and, because they are unnatural, they can easily become 'monocultures'. A monoculture is a habitat where only one type of plant can be found. Plants like Canadian pondweed, for example, can grow and develop so fast that they choke out other plants. They may need to be cleared out periodically before they make the canal impassable.

The different plants are adapted, not just to the general habitat, but to the micro-habitats of deep water and the canal or stream banks. Shallow-water plants have long underground stems to hold them upright and out of the water. The familiar example is the reedmace, with its paintbrush-like seedhead. Deep-water plants may float in the water, with most of the plant under the surface – just the flowers in the air. Some – like the frogbit – float in the water. Floating duckweed can cover a stream but seldom flowers. Alongside the banks, strong, well-rooted plants spread broad leaves.

Ducks of all kinds, moorhens and coots (their white head spots making them look 'as bald as a coot') nest in streams and canals. A mammal that is well adapted to living close to water is the water vole – 'Ratty' from 'The Wind in the Willows'.

## Salt water

### Beaches

The beach is a huge habitat – one long nature reserve stretching all round the coast. Beaches can be sandy or rocky, or flat and muddy. They have lots of plants and animals – even those that look empty! Beach animals hide from the Sun under rocks. Some shellfish, worms and crabs bury themselves in the sand. The rock pool is home to many animals and plants – a micro-habitat.

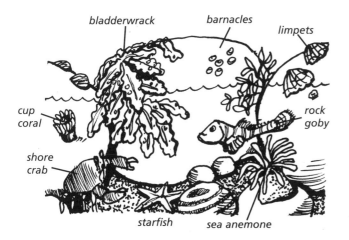

bladderwrack   barnacles   limpets   cup coral   rock goby   shore crab   starfish   sea anemone

The beach is an extraordinarily varied habitat, changing completely as the tide comes and goes twice a day. Beach plants and animals have adapted to this constant change and this has led to zonation – the beach has a series of zones, from underwater to 'splash zone', and animals and plants find their own level in this horizontal system. The more exposure an animal or plant can stand, the higher up the beach it will be.

### Estuaries

Britain has over 160 estuaries, which represent a unique and rewarding habitat. Many are still unaffected by people, and so are a natural habitat, as many grasslands, woodlands and hedgerows are not. Because of the tidal changes and other special conditions, animals and plants living in estuaries are uniquely adapted. Both the tides and the seasons present dramatic changes.

*Look for these in the estuary or on the beach.*

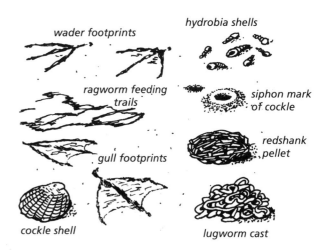

wader footprints   hydrobia shells   ragworm feeding trails   siphon mark of cockle   gull footprints   redshank pellet   cockle shell   lugworm cast

Fresh water and salt water mix in estuaries. This makes life difficult for creatures adapting to the changing salinity; but the estuarine habitat is rich and fertile. As many as 20,000 small creatures may live in every square metre of estuary mud, which represents a calorific value of more than a dozen Mars bars.

The tides present twice-daily changes in temperature and dryness to which plants and animals must adapt.

The mud brought down by the river settles in stages; the finer mud near the river, the coarser, sandy mud near the mouth of the estuary. Flowering plants take hold on higher ground around estuary edges, forming a special habitat called a salt marsh. This has its own unique flora and fauna. Salt marshes may be grazed by cattle or sheep – behind the protection of a sea wall.

## The sea

Seas and other water cover three-quarters of our planet. Two-thirds of the Earth is covered by water that is more than 100 metres deep. Until very recently, we have known little about the seas and oceans and even less about what happens in the deepest sea. We have better maps of the surface of the Moon than we have of the sea floor.

We do know that there are mountains under the sea in places as high – and even higher – than those on land. There are underwater volcanoes and in places on the ridges that mark the mid-oceans, there are great spouts of incredibly hot water called hydrothermal vents. In this amazing world live a whole flora and fauna that have yet to be fully discovered and described.

The plants growing in the sea may be familiar seashore algae – the seaweeds – or they may be microscopic floating phytoplankton. Both of these play the same role as green plants on land; they are able to take water and carbon dioxide and, using energy from the Sun, they can convert these to the other, more complex materials that are the first step in almost every food chain.

But not quite every food chain. A unique collection of bacteria are to be found around the hydrothermal vents. They can live in the superheated water and take simple chemicals like methane and hydrogen sulphide from it to turn into complex food materials. These bacteria become food to shrimps, clams and worms of all kinds.

Other animals browse on the seaweeds and the phytoplankton and they are eaten in turn by larger predators.

### Fascinating facts

- Wetlands are areas of marsh or swamp. They are home to hippos, crocodiles and many types of birds and fish. Cypress trees in the wetlands can clean up domestic sewage, binding up harmful nitrates in their roots. Wetlands have been called 'the Earth's kidneys'.

- New islands are forming all the time as the sea level changes. In 1963, a new island called Surtsey appeared off the coast of Iceland when a volcano erupted. It offers a new and unspoiled habitat to plants and animals.

Many of the deep-sea creatures are so unusual that they are difficult to classify. There are groups of animals living in the sea that are not found in any other habitat; the starfish group, for example, that also includes the sea urchins, the sea cucumbers and the stalked sea lilies.

There are groups of animals that grow and branch (like plants); or that live in huge colonies (like corals); and there are creatures like the barnacles that spend the early part of their lives as free-swimming animals, only to find a suitable rock and cement themselves to it, spending the rest of their lives 'lying on their backs and kicking their food into their mouths'.

There are sea mammals – including whales, dolphins and porpoise and seals. There are fish of two kinds – the cartilaginous fish like the sharks and rays, whose bones resemble the bendy material in our ears and noses, and the bony fish with hard skeletons. But by far the largest number of sea animals are the invertebrates – some with a hard outside skeleton, like crabs and lobster; some with hard shells; some who live in protected colonies like the corals; and some with no hard skeleton at all – the jellyfish among them.

### Coral reefs

Coral reefs look like gardens under the sea. They contain millions of living organisms and support millions of others. A coral reef can take hundreds of years to form. Coral is made from the lime skeleton of tiny sea animals called polyps, related to sea anemones and jellyfish. The coral polyps have green algae living in them that remove their carbon dioxide and give them nutrients in return. The fish that shelter in the corals produce waste products, rich in nutrients, that help the corals grow faster. The lives of all these creatures are linked very closely together.

# Land habitats

## Hedgerows

A hedgerow is a habitat. Many plants and animals live in hedges, which form long nature reserves in many parts of the country.

- Some animals (hover-flies, beetles, bush crickets and yellowhammers) live on the top or the outside of the hedge.
- Others (aphids, caterpillars and hedge-sparrows) live in the depths of its leaves and branches.
- Some (millipedes, slugs, ground-beetles and hedgehogs) live under the hedge.
- Others (wasps, rabbits, bank voles and shrews) live in burrows in the ground beneath the hedge.

### Fascinating facts

- Yaks live in one of the world's highest habitats. They eat the plants that grow 4,500 metres up in the mountains.

- We removed 8,000km of hedge every year between 1945 and 1974. We still destroy more than 3,000km of hedge every year – the distance from London to Cairo.

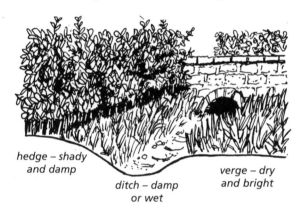

hedge – shady and damp

ditch – damp or wet

verge – dry and bright

Many hedges are hundreds of years old. It takes time for new plants to establish themselves in a hedge, so one way of estimating the age of a hedge is to count all the different types of plants in the hedge. As a rule of thumb, each new species of large, established plant represents 100 years. So a hedge in which you pass three different established plants in a few yards is probably around 300 years old.

Hedges shelter farm animals from the wind and help prevent land erosion. They are home to many plants and animals, including important pollinators and pest predators. Hedges produce timber, fruit and nuts.

## Grasslands

There are many grasslands. These enormous fields have different names. In Africa and Australia they're called savannahs, in Europe and Asia they are called steppes and in South America they are called pampas.

Many animals on grasslands live in large groups or herds. Once, huge herds of bison roamed the grasslands of North America. Herds of antelope and zebra still feed on the grasslands of Africa. Herd animals survive

because they can protect themselves better in a large group. Their young are able to run almost from birth. Many of these herd animals eat grass. Other animals survive because they can burrow. Ground squirrels and rabbits dig deep into the ground. Their young are often born helpless – blind and hairless – because they are safe in the burrows. These burrowing animals may eat grass or live on seeds. Small burrowing mammals – mice and shrews – bury the seeds for winter food.

There are many predators on the grasslands from the dog and cat families. There are hunting dogs, coyotes, foxes and dingoes, and cats, such as lions, cheetahs and puma.

## Fields

All fields may look alike to you but fields – even those that are apparently 'just grass' – can be very different and be planted for very different purposes.

School fields and sports fields are managed to provide a surface for outdoor activities. They may be treated for moss and wildflowers, 'weed' treated round the edges, and mown – often not as frequently as you might like. As a result, you may have a field that is largely grass – and very dull grass at that. You may be totally unaware that it has an animal life at all – until one spring morning when the whole field sparkles with dewy cobwebs.

On hay meadows, grass is left until the seed heads have ripened, when it is cut, dried and stored for winter feed. As it grows, a hay field provides an excellent habitat for wild plants, insects, birds and small mammals.

Grass is a flowering plant. Grass flowers are not brightly coloured, since they don't attract insects for pollination. The green flowers shed a wealth of pollen, as asthma and hay fever sufferers will know. The wind-borne pollen is filtered from the air by long, tassel-like stigmata. The grass seeds form, producing on some 'grasses' most of the staple food sources – wheat, rice, oats, barley and sweetcorn among them.

Because they find little shelter from predators, the animals in fields are cleverly adapted to hide or take flight. The fieldmouse makes a tiny nest in long grass. The hare has an open nest and can run at very high speeds. Skylarks have open nests, too, and tricks for protecting their eggs and young – pretending to have a broken wing, for example, to attract predators away from the nest.

## Woodlands

The first trees colonised the UK after the Ice Age, about 8000BCE. At that time, the British Isles were still physically joined to the continental mainland. The first trees produced a natural forest called the wildwood. It was 5,000 years before humans began to affect the wildwood – clearing it for cultivation. Today, Britain is one of the least wooded countries in Europe.

Some woods today are directly descended from the wildwood. Others have grown naturally on heath or grassland. Many have been deliberately planted – like the huge areas of conifer plantation. Even ancient woods have been carefully managed by people to produce wood for fuel and building, for fences and tools. Coppicing and pollarding have resulted in managed growth.

### Fascinating facts

- Half the plants and animals known live in the rainforests. The layers of the rainforest from treetops to forest floor offer a huge range of habitats and invite a huge range of living things.

- Badlands are the barren, rocky parts of the world where dinosaurs once roamed. Some plants – like juniper and sage – can survive the heat, and a few animals – like reptiles, antelope and eagles – live in the badlands.

Wildwood indicators include trees like the woodland hawthorn, the wild lime and the wild service tree. Wood anemone, wood sorrel, wood speedwell and yellow pimpernel may also identify ancient woodland.

Squirrels and mice live in, or on, the trees of a woodland. Birds adapted to a woodland include the woodpecker, which eats insects from dead trees, and the tree-creeper, which can make its way up and down trees. Every woodland has an all-rounder. In parts of France, wild boar eat both nuts and fungi as well as small animals, such as insects, frogs and mice, which are unable to get away. There is some talk about reintroducing wild boar – and even wolves – into the UK.

## Forests

The rainforests are close to the Equator. The rainforests are hot and wet. There are no seasons. Two metres of rain may fall every year. Many trees in the rainforests have waxy leaves that let the rain run off. There is a rich animal life in the dense foliage, and the trees make layers.

Rainforest animals include browsers, such as the sloths and monkeys; predators, like the eagles; and scavengers, like the beetles that clear the forest floor. At night, pottos, bush-babies and lorises use their huge eyes to find insects in the dark. Fruit-eating bats live in the trees.

Temperate forests are warm in summer and cool in winter. They are huge areas of broad-leafed trees, shading the ground beneath them. They are home to deer and hunters such as weasels, wild cats and martens. The raccoon eats almost anything in the US forests, from fruit to mice.

Pine trees grow in coniferous forests. Because they are evergreens, the ground beneath them is always in shade. Few plants grow. Pine trees are resistant to wind. Not having the large leaves of deciduous trees, they let the wind whistle through their branches, and are undisturbed by high mountain conditions.

They are home to hardier animals – larger deer, foxes and some big cats.

## Walls

Even schools in the most urban conditions can find places where wildlife flourishes. Walls, with their exposure to the Sun and natural drainage, are welcoming environments to many plants and animals. Mosses can find points of attachment, and smaller invertebrates can slip into cracks and crevices. Because they warm quickly, walls can be attractive to 'cold-blooded' animals like lizards.

## Rubbish dumps

It is a sad fact of life that if you want to see a bear in Canada, you are as likely to find it at the local tip as in the Rockies. Canadian bears, like urban foxes, are finding that a good meal is available in human refuse. Seagulls, driven inland by winter storms, live by scavenging on rubbish dumps. Huge numbers of micro-organisms that we depend upon for the decay of waste are hard at work in landfill sites. The waste products in these sites include methane, which, if not carefully piped and burned off, can lead to an explosion of millions of disposable nappies – a contemporary experiment in wrapping human waste in polythene and dumping it that may yet – literally – backfire on us.

## Hot places

Deserts are places with no water, or very little water. Even if it rains, the water will evaporate before it can sink in. Some deserts are sandy and the sand can be blown around by the wind. Others are rocky. The Sahara desert can be as hot as 58°C.

But the hottest deserts can be freezing cold at night, so it is hard for plants and animals to survive. Desert animals can aestivate – remain inactive – in hot weather. They slow their body processes almost to a standstill. Lung-fish can survive for years in a narrow tunnel in this state, without food or water. They have even been canned and sent great distances, to arrive alive. When the rain returns, the animals react very quickly. The African bullfrog hatches the day after rain. It becomes an adult in four weeks, mates, lays its eggs, and buries itself in the mud again.

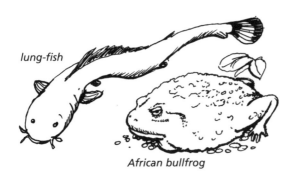

lung-fish

African bullfrog

You might look at a desert and think it was lifeless. But after heavy rain, desert pools can be full of water fleas, shrimps, tadpoles and even fish!

## Cold places

There are long winters and short summers at both the Arctic and the Antarctic. There is no sun in the winter and it is very low in the summer. It is freezing all year round. Arctic flowers may turn to face the sun. This keeps the flower warm to attract insects. Animals may migrate or hibernate – even penguins may migrate to warmer places. Fat layers insulate creatures like the seal, stopping the animal losing heat. Thick fur insulates the polar bear, too. All polar mammals have small ears, because you lose a lot of heat through your ears. Many polar animals have a kind of antifreeze in their blood.

The tundra is an area of cold wind and little rain. The plants are low and cushion-shaped to resist the wind. Insects survive under the soil as eggs or pupae. Birds find plenty of food on the tundra and the long summer days make it easy to collect food to rear their young.

Over millions of years, water trickling through soft rocks like limestone cuts caves in them. The caves are light at the entrance, then there is a 'twilight' zone, and then darkness. Animals living in the dark zone are prisoners of the darkness. The fish, crayfish, insects and spiders that live there are colourless and blind. They find their way by touch. There are no plants. Food is washed in by streams and rain.

The air is thin on mountains, and there is little flat ground. The few plants that grow are low. Trees are shorter on mountains than they would be lower down. Mountain mammals are adapted to living on uneven surfaces and mountain birds nest on the ground rather than in trees.

You are unlikely to have a habitat quite as exotic as some of these on your doorstep, but there will be rich animal and plant life not far from you. It is just a question of finding it.

## Fascinating facts

- Desert plants are often small, with a small surface area to reduce the loss of water. Their long roots penetrate deep in the desert. The animals that dodge their spines to browse on them may get all their water from plant tissue.

- Squirrels in cold habitats use their tails to wrap round themselves and keep themselves warm. The ground squirrel has adapted its behaviour to living in a sunny habitat. It uses its tail as an umbrella to shelter from the sun.

- The tundra is frozen soil and the habitat is cold and severe. Mosses and sedges are the plants that can survive here, together with animals like hares and weasels. Lemmings are important to the tundra regions as their manure stimulates plant growth in these bleak surroundings.

- About 800 species of plant can survive the low temperatures in Antarctica. Lichens, moulds, algae and liverworts cover the dark-coloured rocks that absorb heat most easily.

# Activities

## Level One

Go for a listening walk. Tell the children that they must be very quiet and try not to make too much noise with their feet. From time to time stop and listen. What animals can they hear? Once all is quiet, they should hear different bird calls. But they might also hear rustling noises of insects and small creatures around them, even if they can't see them. Use a tape recorder to record the sounds and play them back in school. Make a labelled frieze of the animals they think they heard. Alternatively make a labelled map of the walk they took and label on it what they heard where.

Record the plants growing near your school. Do the same for small invertebrates – find and record them, but do not collect them.

## Level Two

What a difference a tree makes. Children will find very different plants and animals close to a tree from those further away. You may find a hoop useful to restrict the search area; or you, or another briefed adult, could help them to look at the differences a tree makes to the surroundings. Ask why. Draw out that a tree shades an area; it may make it drier; that the roots under the ground cover an area at least as big as the tree in the sky.

Match animals with their habitats. Why do they live where they do? What does the habitat offer them? Why is it the animal's 'address'?

## Level Three

Explore the ways that plants and animals suit their habitat. Notice that the animals living on walls are often flat from top to bottom, such as the earwig and woodlice. Animals living in damp places, such as slugs and worms, have moist, sticky skins that help them to retain water should their habitat dry out.

Ask groups of children to adopt a habitat – local or farther afield. Ask them to research the animals and plants that live there. Then they present their habitat to the others in the class. Compare the habitats and how the plants and animals have adapted.

## Level Four

Explore the ways that plants and animals in a habitat depend upon each other – the way that insects carry pollen but are also fed by the plants they visit. Look at feeding relationships – food chains that begin with a green plant.

## Level Five

Look at the environmental factors that determine why certain plants and animals live in particular places. Compare two habitats, for example a wooded area and a more open habitat. Notice that plants in wooded areas often grow from bulbs, which give them an early start before the trees shade them and they also flower early.

Look at the factors that determine why frogs may be found in one pond but not another, or small creatures on one side of a wall but not the other.

Relate the animals and plants found in a habitat to the factors affecting that habitat. Link together food chains in the same habitat to form more complex food webs. Explain why there are fewer predators than prey.

# Why don't lions eat oranges?

**Because they can't peel them, silly!**

There are food chains in every habitat that ensure that organisms survive. You can see these food chains as a sort of energy flow and, ultimately, all that energy begins with the Sun. It is the Sun's energy that plants convert to their own structures, and hence to food. Green plants are the first link in most food chains.

## Food chains

After green plants, the next link is the plant-eaters. Finally, predators live off plant-eaters and also off each other.

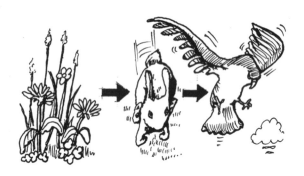

Food chains show how plants are eaten by plant-eaters, and plant-eaters are eaten by meat-eaters. But it isn't quite as simple as that. Food chains with the direct line of the grass – zebra – lion type are uncommon.

## Food webs

It is easier to understand this in terms of food webs. Aphids live off plants and ladybirds live off aphids. But the ladybird could meet any number of fates from insect-eating birds, who might themselves take a fancy to a juicy aphid…

A food web shows the animals that might live on or around a tree for example. In every food web, there are many different food chains. The food web in a woodland, for example, might involve some plant-eating consumers – grasshoppers and mice. A secondary consumer like a frog might not tackle a mouse, but will make a meal of a grasshopper. Snakes are partial to frogs, but not averse to a mouse – or a grasshopper – either. Hawks will eat a snake – or jump that link and go straight for a mouse.

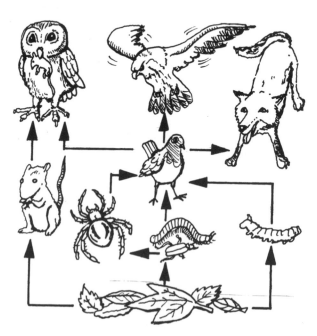

So although the flow of energy through natural chains may be short, it is far from simple.

### Fascinating facts

- 2.6 million tonnes of pesticides are applied every year around the world.

- 23,000 tonnes of pesticide are sprayed on UK crops every year.

- Since pesticides were reintroduced in the 40s to help with the effects of intensive farming, flowering plants in fields have become a rare sight. The knock-on effects of killing insects and seed-bearing weeds have had an effect on birds. In the past 25 years, 89% of tree sparrows, 73% of song thrushes and 77% of turtledoves have been lost due to this.

## Seaside food webs

All animals have to eat. Some eat plants; some eat other animals. Some, like us, may eat both. Some sea creatures also eat detritus, a mixture of microscopic plant and animal remains that we might think was waste. But nothing is wasted in the sea and even this waste material has a place in the food web.

An estuarine food web, like almost all food webs, starts with the Sun. Tiny floating plants use sunlight to turn water and carbon dioxide gas into food. Tiny animals eat the plants. Worms and shellfish filter the animals and plants from the water and eat them. Crabs eat the worms and shellfish. Some birds, like the ringed plover, will eat the bigger animals. Shellfish filter detritus – plant and animal waste – from the seawater.

The same thing happens in rock pools. Seaweeds can use the Sun's light to make their own food. Tiny floating plants can use the Sun's light to make their own food, too. Periwinkles eat seaweeds. Dog-whelks eat periwinkles. Birds like the oyster-catcher eat periwinkles. Barnacles filter tiny floating plants from seawater. Sea squirts filter tiny floating plants from seawater.

In the deep oceans, one humpback whale needs about 5,000 herring every day to feed it. Each herring will have eaten about 7,000 shrimps. Each shrimp will have eaten as many as 130,000 tiny green plants. This means that it takes about four billion tiny plants (4,000,000,000) to feed a humpback whale for one day. This change in numbers is called a food pyramid – and this is a pretty extreme example!

### Fascinating facts

- Oranges have up to nine pesticides sprayed on them before they reach the shops. After harvest, oranges may be washed in chlorinated water and detergent, then sprayed with fungicide and coated in wax to make them shiny.

- Carrots contain up to 29 different pesticides, including organophosphates (also used in sheep-dips).

- Growing the food required to feed one American person causes about 15 tonnes of soil erosion annually.

## Food pyramids

What is certain is that there needs to be more grass than rabbits and more rabbits than foxes or hawks. This increase in relative numbers as you go down the energy flow results in the food pyramid – hawk at the top, rabbits in the middle, plants at the bottom.

## Food chains shape animals

Animals are unable to make their own food so they have had to develop ways of moving to food sources (or, in the case of sessile animals like barnacles and sea anemones, ways of catching passing food).

Once a living thing moves, it needs sense organs to find its way around. Putting the sense organs at the front or top of the body makes them more useful. If the animal is a secondary consumer – a predator or carnivore – the sense organs are likely to be forward-facing, enabling it to see its prey and to catch it efficiently. If the animal is a primary consumer or herbivore, then its sense organs are likely to survey the surroundings more generally, because it needs to be aware of predators and danger. Cats have eyes on the front of their heads; mice have them on the side. Cats have excellent, stereoscopic forward vision to catch mice; mice have good all-round vision to spot and avoid cats.

Food also shapes animal chemistry. Humans are unable to store vitamin C. We don't need to, as long as we eat fresh fruit and vegetables daily. But carnivores don't eat apples or salad, so they have to find their vitamin C from other sources. They are able to utilise the vitamin C of their prey animals, which keeps them healthy. So lions don't need to eat oranges!

## Short but not so sweet

Most food chains are very short. Phytoplankton (planktonic plants) float in the lighter surface waters of the sea. They harness the Sun's energy through photosynthesis to produce oxygen and to live and grow. They produce oxygen as a waste product. The phytoplankton are food for other living things. Krill are small shrimp-like crustaceans that feed on phytoplankton. Whales feed by eating huge quantities of krill. (Blue whales can eat four tonnes of krill every day.)

Other creatures eat phytoplankton, including a lot of the sea's filter feeders – shellfish and small fish. They might be eaten in turn by gulls, turtles and other sea creatures. These interlinking food chains become a food web.

## Except...

Not all food chains start with a green plant. There are deep-sea life forms that can harness chemical energy. These bacteria live in total darkness near the hydrothermal vents of the Pacific Ocean, in very high temperatures. Deep-sea animals eat the bacteria as other animals eat plants.

## Concentrated pollutant

Food chains can concentrate pollutants. The chemical DDT was hailed as an answer to pest problems in crops. But DDT has an unfortunate characteristic. It concentrates in the bodies of animals. It was bad enough for the plant-eaters; but much worse for the carnivores.

Small animals accumulated small amounts of DDT, an insecticide that was first discovered in 1939 and used to control the insects that spread malaria. While it did the small animals little harm, it didn't leave their bodies, either. They were eaten in large numbers by birds of prey and other predators. As a result, these animals got heavy – sometimes fatal – doses. Its use was banned in most countries when this environmental concentration was discovered. The powerful book by Rachel Carson – 'Silent Spring' – that was sparked by this event was one of the first to draw our attention to environmental damage.

## Fascinating facts

- Genetically modified potatoes in the USA have been modified to resist the Colorado potato beetle which has been classified as a pest.

- Almost all food webs start with the Sun. But at the bottom of the deepest seas, where it is always pitch dark, creatures called bacteria make food using simple substances like hydrogen sulphide – which smells of bad eggs – and methane gas. Shrimps feed on the bacteria, and other animals eat the shrimps.

- The food chain concept was first described by a German zoologist, Karl Semper, in 1891.

- Food webs, because they mean that animals are eating more than one food, are more stable than food chains.

# Activities

## Level One

Using pictures of living things, define plants, plant-eaters and meat-eaters. Ask the children to sort them into these groups, giving reasons for their choice. Explain that there are some animals – humans , pigs and bears – that eat both plants and animals. You might introduce words like 'herbivore', 'carnivore' and 'omnivore' if your children like rolling their tongues round long words like these.

Put labels on the backs of three or four children. The labels name a plant or animal. These children are allowed to ask questions, in turn, either of the rest of the class, or of a group of classmates. The questions must be answerable with a 'yes' or a 'no'. 'Do I eat grass?' for example, or 'Do I live in trees?' As they get close to their identity, they can ask 'Am I a …?' In the game, they begin to identify the unique qualities of each animal and plant.

## Level Two

Give children the identities of plants and animals. They keep them secret, but must answer the questions of other children in turn, while asking their own. The aim is to find out what another child is supposed to be and then either to 'eat' them – hold them by the wrist – or get away. Predators will do best, of course.

Think of several potential chains with no more than three or four links, such as 'Foxes eat rabbits eat grass.' Make cards for the different parts of the food chain and give them out to the children. For example, include some cards saying 'hawk', some saying 'mouse' and some saying 'acorn'. Ask the children to run around in an open area. At a signal, they are to form a chain – three people together that might represent a food chain. The first formed chain – 'cat – bird – seed', for example – wins. Introduce the words 'producer' and 'consumer'.

## Level Three

Play the game as described for Level 2, but this time add unlikely links to the chains – broadening the range of plants and animals. This time, the chains must make sense; 'seaweed – fish – seal' makes sense but 'seaweed – rabbit – seal' does not. As the game progresses, point out that some of the chains can vary – a snake might eat a frog or a grasshopper, so that you could have a four-link chain: 'plant – grasshopper – frog – snake'. Explain that this leads to food webs – and show some examples.

## Level Four

Use a long piece of string or a ball of wool to demonstrate the interdependence of living things in a food web. The children circle the holder of the ball, who represents the Sun. Each child holds an animal or plant name card – tree, grass, flower, caterpillar, frog, hare, rabbit, fox, hawk and so on. The ball is passed to the producers and unrolled as it goes. So from the Sun it goes to all the plants. Then from them it goes to all the plant-eaters/primary consumers and then finally to all the meat-eaters/ secondary consumers. A real 'web' is produced. Then you can choose to remove some links. The hare drops his or her string. Who is affected? (By dropping different parts of the web, you can demonstrate both interdependence and environmental damage.)

## Level Five

Use a game that shows how pollution can accumulate in a food web. You need 100 scraps of paper. These are phytoplankton. They are tiny green plants that float about in the sea. Put a coloured spot on half these pieces of paper. That is pollution! Half of the children are barnacles – animals that are glued by their backs to a rock, kicking their food into their mouths!

Most of the people who are left are wrasse – fish with strong jaws that can break open and eat barnacles. Two of those left are seals. Seals eat fish, including wrasse. One person is a dolphin. Dolphins eat fish and seals.

Now the game starts. Scatter the paper scraps on the floor, spotty side down! The barnacles get one minute to 'eat' – pick up – as many 'phytoplankton' as they can. They look at their catch. Have they eaten much pollution?

The barnacles are free to choose a place to sit down. The wrasse are free to go and 'eat' – touch – one or more barnacles. When a barnacle is touched, it gives up its papers. The wrasse look at their catch. How many have swallowed pollution? Now the wrasse run away while the seals chase them. If a wrasse is caught, it gives up its papers. How much pollution have the seals swallowed? Any uneaten wrasse stay in the game. Lastly a dolphin tries to catch a seal or a wrasse. If a wrasse or a seal is caught, it gives up its papers. What pollution has the dolphin eaten? Ask the children what has happened. How has the pollution passed through the food chain? How has it become concentrated?

# Micro-organisms

## Why bugs?

Children call micro-organisms 'bugs' or 'germs'. These names include small invertebrates, bacteria and viruses and are associated with dirt, death and disease. Children may think of micro-organisms as things that walk about inside us, eating, breeding and making us ill. Given the opportunity, they would probably exterminate all micro-organisms, thus inadvertently bringing the world to a speedy end!

Few children are aware of the beneficial effects of micro-organisms and they have little idea of their importance in decay and recycling. They may not understand that we live our lives surrounded by micro-organisms of all sorts, and that we are dependent on them for our health and wellbeing.

It's difficult to teach about micro-organisms, because you're teaching about something that is invisible to the naked eye. It's very hard to envisage a microscopic world of the size and complexity that exists and harder still to give children experience of it.

In promoting the benefits of micro-organisms, point out that they are essential to making leavened bread, cheese, yoghurt, vinegar, yeast extract or Marmite, and many protein meat substitutes. They are essential to the production of many medicines, the breakdown of sewage and the production of silage, the 'pickled grass' used as winter cattle food.

## Bugs are best

### Inside a cow!

For an example of the impact of micro-organisms on our lives, consider the origins of that yoghurt in the fridge. It all starts at the farm. Cows eat silage – a kind of pickled grass. The action of bacteria on cut grass in anaerobic (oxygenless) conditions is to make it slightly acidic, and this acid works just like the vinegar in pickle, preventing further decay, and making the food more palatable. The cows' stomach bacteria act on the grass during digestion, breaking down the tough plant cells. From the silage, cows produce milk.

Most milk is pasteurised to destroy the natural bacteria that lead to milk going off. This is the treatment of the milk – momentarily – with a very high temperature. There will be inevitable decay, but pasteurising or UHT treatment slows this. Special bacteria have to be added to make yoghurt. There is evidence that every civilisation has found ways of conserving milk by making another product – yoghurt, cheese – from it. It may be that they learned this art from the natural fermentation of milk – perhaps in a bag made from the stomach of an animal.

### Inside you!

Your gut bacteria help you to digest your food, including the yoghurt. We have a wonderful flora in our intestines which helps us to digest our food – a Balti meal will lead to an explosion of special bacteria to cope with it! Finally, bacteria at the sewage farm break down human waste into a safe form to be returned to the cycle, and the waste from the cows fertilises the fields to grow next year's grass.

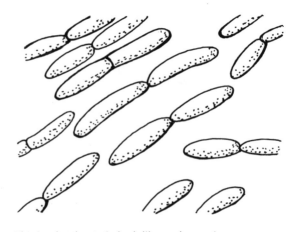

*This is what bacteria look like under a microscope.*

## Biotechnology

The application of micro-organisms – biotechnology – is a major growth area in science. A wide range of foods – leavened bread, wine, beer, vinegar, and vegetable protein – is dependent on our understanding of the action of micro-organisms.

## What is yeast?

Yeast is a living organism – a type of fungus – that can be safely grown in the classroom. You may be able to buy fresh bread yeast but more likely you will find dried yeast in the shops, in packets or drums. Given warmth, moisture and food, living yeast cells will respire and give off carbon dioxide gas.

If you half-fill a small plastic bottle with warm water (blood heat, the temperature of your hand), add a teaspoonful of dried yeast and a teaspoonful of sugar, plug the top with cotton wool (which allows gases in and out, but keeps out other micro-organisms), shake the bottle gently, leave it in a warm place and watch, you will see yeast at work.

You will see that bubbles of gas (carbon dioxide) are produced as the yeast respires. Warming the water increases the rate of respiration, while letting it cool slows it. Water that is too hot kills the yeast and there is no bubbling.

Fermenting yeast is used to raise bread and other dough mixtures. The yeast goes on producing carbon dioxide gas until alcohol – a product of its anaerobic respiration – builds up in the bottle and kills the yeast.

To see yeast cells – which look like bunches of grapes – you need a magnifier.

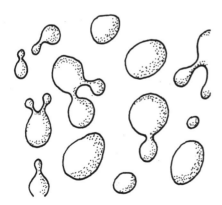

*This is what yeast cells look like under a microscope.*

### Fascinating facts

- 160,000 million bacteria could fit in a teaspoon.

- 500 bacteria would fit, side by side, across a full stop.

- Bacteria divide so fast that one could become one thousand million in 15 hours.

- Some bacteria swim 100 times their own length in a second.

- Some bacteria can 'eat stone'. They produce sulphuric acid which breaks marble down to softer plaster. Carbon dioxide gas is given off which the bacteria use in their nutrition. The hard stone rots away.

## What causes illness?

Illnesses like the common cold, mumps and tooth decay are caused by micro-organisms. Vaccination, or immunisation, helps prevent illnesses (infection with diseases) by giving humans or other animals mild forms of the illness and building up their immunity. Cooking food thoroughly, storing it carefully to prevent the growth of micro-organisms, washing hands before handling food, not sharing each other's drink bottles and cutlery and washing hands after visiting the toilet all help prevent food poisoning.

## Preserving food

Decay is caused by micro-organisms. They like damp, warm conditions with plenty of food. In those conditions they will grow, reproduce, and cause decay. They don't like it dry or cold and they don't like vinegar or strong sugar solutions.

Dried food is not damp enough for decay. Canned food has usually been cooked and then quickly sealed. There are no living micro-organisms in it. Pickled food is in vinegar and micro-organisms cannot live in the acid. Jam has a lot of sugar in it and is not wet enough for micro-organisms to grow. But notice what happens if you get a sticky puddle with less sugar form on top of the jam. Mould (fungus) grows in the puddle.

Fridges and freezers are too cold for micro-organisms to live in and reproduce quickly. But they still cause decay – eventually.

# Smallpox and cowpox

The story of Edward Jenner and smallpox vaccination is well known, but what might not be so clear is why a mother was happy to allow her young son to be used for a dangerous medical experiment. The truth is fascinating, and more complicated than you might expect.

We don't fear smallpox these days. It has been virtually eradicated and the only smallpox bacteria on Earth are locked away in chemical warfare laboratories. But in 1796 it was a scourge – especially of the young – so severe that some families, wishing to continue a family name, would call more than one son or daughter by the same name so that if they lost one child to smallpox, another would carry it on. Survivors of the disease were horribly scarred by the pustules.

But a remarkable woman named Lady Mary Wortley Montague had recently returned from Greece, where she had accompanied her husband. There she had observed the process of 'ingrafting', where young children were infected with smallpox pus, sometimes slightly heated to weaken it, by rubbing it into scratches in their arm. The children were mildly infected – and some died – but those that recovered were then immune from the disease. Smallpox seldom attacked the same person twice.

Lady Mary returned to England, where she 'ingrafted' her own children successfully and introduced the practice to her friends. Soon, smallpox 'farms' sprang up where children could be ingrafted and made immune from the disease. It became fashionable among the wealthy to send your children to these places. But there were still occasional deaths.

It was the chance remark of Sarah Nelmes, the milkmaid, to Edward Jenner, the country doctor, that set in train the events that led to vaccination. She commented that since she had cowpox – a mild cattle disease caught from the udders of cows, that had brought up pustules on her hands – she would not catch smallpox. Jenner linked this to his understanding of ingrafting, and so one local mother, a Mrs Phipps, was very happy to have her son James treated with cowpox pus rather than sent to a smallpox farm. Jenner infected James with cowpox. The lad was poorly for a while. Then he ingrafted James with smallpox. The disease did not develop. James had been 'vaccinated' – treated by a cow.

On June 25, 1796, Jenner announced that vaccination had prevented James Phipps catching smallpox. Wealthy families took it up and Princess Caroline – the Diana, Princess of Wales of her time – had her children vaccinated, giving it national importance. In 1840, the Government passed the Vaccination Act, so that everyone in Britain was freed from the danger of smallpox. Other countries followed suit. The disease was completely eradicated in 1979.

Now only two known stores of smallpox germs exist – held by Russia and the USA in the ceaseless research into chemical warfare. Now what would Jenner have thought of that?

---

### References

Useful websites can be found through the Royal Microscopical Society website: www.rms.org.uk/

If you use Yahoo as your search engine, try: www.yahoo.co.uk/Science/Engineering/ Optical_Engineering/Microscopy/

There is a wealth of information on the Internet. Use the words microscope, bacteria or similar to find more information.

The Royal Microscopical Society offers a programme of educational activities. They also sometimes run initiatives to encourage primary schools to buy microscopes. For example, they have previously refunded £20 for each RMS-approved microscope (costing around £50) purchased, subject to a limit of 2 per school and the availability of funds. The Royal Microscopical Society, 37–38 St Clements, Oxford OX4 1AJ, Tel 01865 248768; Fax 01865 791237; e-mail info@RMS.org.uk

# Activities

## Level One

Teach the children to use a magnifying glass correctly – by lifting objects to their eye rather than bending over them and blocking all the light.

Use a magnifying glass for close observation of plants and small creatures.

## Level Two

Help the children to use a binocular microscope for close observation – including creatures swimming in water. They should then draw what they see and identify it. Investigate the idea that there may be living things even smaller than these.

## Level Three

Ask the children to find out the part played by micro-organisms in making bread, Quorn – artificial protein – cheese and vinegar.

Investigate some mushrooms. (Make sure the children do not eat anything that is picked. Warn them of the danger of poisoning.) Mushrooms are large, edible fungi. They are in the same broad group – the Protista – as yeast, bacteria, and viruses. Draw them, cut them in half, draw the insides. Leave some on paper overnight, with a cover against draughts. You will see dark or cream coloured spores the next day, reflecting the mushroom's radial pattern.

Arrange for a chiropodist or school nurse to explain about athlete's foot – a fungal disease that damages the skin between the toes. Bacteria enter the damaged skin, causing a fierce itching. Explain how important it is to dry your feet after washing; damp, warm conditions suit fungi!

## Level Four

Discuss yeast with the children. What do they know? They may come up with, or you may explain that, yeast is a living organism; yeast cells are too tiny to see – except under the microscope; yeast makes bread rise and ferments wine and beer; yeast feeds on sugar; yeast produces a gas (carbon dioxide); dried yeast appears dead. It needs moisture to show signs of life.

Provide strong glass bottles, warm tap water, sugar and cotton wool. The cotton wool is for stopping the bottles. (DO NOT ALLOW BOTTLE TOPS. The enclosed gas could explode.)

Ask the children to prove that living yeast produces a gas in warm, wet conditions, but that hot conditions kill yeast. Allow some planning. Agree the plan before the children start.

A bottle of water at body temperature with yeast cells and sugar (a dough starter) will soon develop a bubbly surface. This isn't direct proof that the yeast is living – baking powder might do the same; but if the children use hot water direct from the tap, the cells are killed and there is no bubbling.

## Level Five

Let the children use secondary sources to research micro-organisms. Find out how they live – and learn that there are many that are beneficial to life. Investigate vaccination.

The air is full of micro-organisms of all kinds. There are many fungal spores that will grow on damp bread. Seal a damp slice of bread in a plastic bag and let the class observe the fungal growth over the next few days. Since you have no control over what grows, you must throw the bag away without opening it.

Consider the conditions necessary for fungal growth. You could set up an investigation with several sealed bags, containing, for example: fresh bread; damp bread; fresh toast; dry bread. Which do the children think will produce the biggest, fastest fungal 'bloom', and why?

You might try growing fungus on the same food in sealed bags, but in different conditions – in the refrigerator, in a warm cupboard, in the classroom. You might try growing fungus on other foods, but do not use anything containing meat. The bags containing the fungus must always be thrown away sealed.